600 PUZZLES

Lateral Thinking Questions and a Treasure Hunt

@ ! * # ?

MALCOLM BRONTE

ISBN: 978-1-7394485-8-5

Printed in the United States of America

Published by Book Marketeers.com

MIDDLEPART
ACADEMY

DEDICATION
&
ACKNOWLEDGMENTS

I would like to acknowledge, and dedicate this book to, all the inspiring, long-suffering and creative people, that have helped me develop and hone the ideas and questions it contains, over the last 40 or 50 years. My family, friends and three decades of university students.

(Remember to have a look at another book published by Middlepart Academy and this author = "More From Life", which includes very different questions and assessments.)

TABLE OF CONTENTS

INTRODUCTION

This is probably the most delightful, amusing, bamboozling, fascinating, tantalizing, stimulating, baffling, entertaining, mysterious, flabbergasting, mind-bending, fiendish and thought-provoking: puzzles, riddles, trivia, detective challenges, perfect crimes, mystery stories, brainteasers, real world intrigues, treasure hunting, creative thinking and problem-solving book, ever!

The 600 questions are designed to be varied, interesting, amusing and challenging. Whether for occasional browsing; or relaxation on a holiday; or enjoyment on a plane or train journey; or as a source of stories, quiz questions and jokes to share with your friends and family; or as a distraction; or as a present for that person, you cannot think what to buy!

The puzzles will entertain you, boost your mental powers, inspire your creativity, encourage you to rethink and test your assumptions and help you to learn to tackle problems in different ways. They promote imagination, ingenuity, originality and inventiveness. Many of them will make you think out-of-the-box. Solving challenging puzzles and exercising your mind have been found to be as good for your brain as running and strength training are for your body.

EXERCISES FOR THE BRAIN

We should give our brain daily doses of exercise. Like our body, our mind requires regular workouts and a good way to do that is to dive into interesting puzzles and games. Keeping your brain active also seems to reduce the risk of developing common causes of mental illness that affect a person's thinking and behavioral skills.

Puzzles stimulate our mind and call for strategic thinking and creative problem solving. The excitement and pleasure of working on the challenges can help to make us feel happier and reduce boredom.

Solving puzzles and tackling lateral thinking problems can:

- improve our concentration, memory and logic;

- help with decision-making;

- give us a sense of satisfaction and accomplishment and

- disrupt our "business-as-usual" way of thinking.

A study involving 2,800 people found that those who did mental exercises such as problem-solving were 29% less likely to develop dementia early. It is known that people who do not smoke, take part in regular physical activity, consume low to moderate amounts of alcohol, adhere to a Mediterranean-style diet, and engage in activities that boost cognitive skills are over 60% less likely to develop Alzheimer's disease.

FRONT COVER

The front cover hints at a popular idea about the human brain – that the left and right hemispheres have different functions and, while both hemispheres are highly interconnected and work together to perform most tasks, each is associated with, particular types of thought processes and behaviors.

The logical, scientific left hemisphere is presumed to be good at:

- Analytical thinking, logical reasoning, mathematical skills, engineering, problem-solving and decision-making.

- Language processing, speech production, language comprehension, reading, and writing.

- Processes information in a sequential and linear manner, focusing on details and step-by-step analysis.

The artistic, imaginative right hemisphere focusses on:

- Creativity, imagination and artistic abilities, painting, colors, music, pattern recognition, making connections and generating ideas.

- Processing and interpretation of emotional information, such as facial expressions and tone of voice.

- Spatial awareness, holistic processing and looking at the "big picture" rather than detailed forensic analysis.

BOOK OUTLINE

The questions in this book cover a wide variety of different topics and types; there is something for everyone. From those that are fun and funny to tricky conundrums and tough-to-solve puzzles. From word games to trivia. From mystery stories and real-world examples to brain-tickling problems. From riddles to mathematical and numerical enigmas. From logic tests to critical and lateral thinking challenges. Many of the questions may seem weird, illogical, bizarre, contradictory or improbable at first, they may look impossible to solve but the more you try, the more you will improve. Many are written in ways that intentionally challenge your assumptions and could send you the wrong way, but all of them include all the information you need.

The first chapter sets the scene and offers 50 relatively easy questions to get you started. After that, the book is chopped into 13 more chapters that cover most types of puzzles and problem-solving questions. Having sharpened your skills, the last chapter includes some really difficult-to-figure-out, brain-crunching questions. The answers to all the questions are at the back of the book followed by the Treasure Hunt.

One of the best ways to enjoy this book is to share it with friends and family. You can either

a) get together and brainstorm answers to questions as you get to them or

b) study and choose questions in advance and challenge your friends to come up with ideas to solve them. This second option is a great way to have fun with some of the trickier lateral thinking problems (such as Caesar and Cleopatra, and the 3 men in a golf club waiting for a parcel, questions) because having read the answer, you can give hints and Yes / No / Not Relevant responses to the questions that others ask on their way to solving these mind-benders. Using the book as a game allows one person to read ahead and act as a quizmaster giving answers and tantalizing hints to the other players in their hunt for the solution. Or split the group into two teams who challenge each other to see how fast they can get an answer. Or make it 20 questions and deduct a point (from 20) for every question asked.

LET'S LOOK AT SOME STYLES OF THINKING

Creative - also known as Unstructured or Free thinking; removing barriers or expanding one's view to look at the "big picture" and consider things in a wider context; encouraging a flurry or blossoming of ideas; a holistic or pluralist approach.

Analytical - also known as Structured or Functional thinking; narrowing in to focus upon specific aspects of the situation; a more scientific, logical, reductionist, or deterministic approach.

Reversal - turning the problem around, looking at it from a different direction and perspective.

Analogy - putting two ideas together to form a third, modeling or adopting other solutions; for example - the function of the heart was only understood when a pump was invented; before that it was thought of as a furnace.

Lateral thinking* - is a problem-solving technique that involves thinking "outside of the box", and exploring new, imaginative, unusual ways of approaching a problem.

Da Vinci's thinking refers to the thought processes and approach to problem-solving inspired by the genius of Leonardo da Vinci, the renowned Italian artist, inventor, and polymath of the Renaissance era. He was known for his insatiable curiosity, observational skills, and ability to connect diverse disciplines and ideas. He questioned everything, exploring and seeking answers through observation, experimentation, and research.

Da Vinci was a master at making connections between different fields of study. He merged art, science, engineering, anatomy, and many other disciplines, understanding that knowledge from one field can inform and inspire innovations in another. His keen powers of observation were central to his artistic and scientific pursuits. He embraced ambiguity and uncertainty. He acknowledged that some problems have multiple solutions and that exploring different possibilities could lead to breakthroughs.

Da Vinci was a **systems thinker**; he recognized the interconnectedness of things and appreciated that problems could not be understood or solved by reducing and isolating them; we need to consider their broader context and relationships. He was a lifelong learner, constantly seeking knowledge and challenging himself. He believed in the importance of self-improvement and personal growth. Da Vinci is famous for his astonishing inventions and imaginative ideas. He embraced experimentation and risk-taking, understanding that failure can be a stepping stone to success. Da Vinci has taught us that:

- Asking thought-provoking questions can lead to new insights and discoveries.

- Interdisciplinary thinking encourages the synthesis of diverse ideas and perspectives.

- Applying visual thinking techniques, such as sketching, diagramming, and mind mapping, can aid in problem-solving and communication.

- Encouraging debate and ambiguity allows for more flexible thinking and creative problem-solving.

- Actively pursuing learning opportunities can lead to continuous development and broader perspectives on problem-solving.

- Developing a mindset of innovation and being open to exploring new approaches that offer novel solutions keeps our thinking dynamic and fresh.

STRATEGIES FOR PROBLEM-SOLVING

Problem-solving is an essential skill for success in both personal and professional contexts. It involves identifying issues, generating ideas, evaluating potential solutions, and implementing the best course of action. There are many problem-solving methods and techniques available to help people address challenges and achieve their objectives. Each method has its strengths and weaknesses, and the most useful approach depends on the nature of the problem and the requirements of the individual or team.

By applying a range of problem-solving methods and techniques, we can approach problems from different angles and create more effective and innovative solutions.

- Brainstorming is a popular problem-solving technique used to generate ideas and solutions through group collaboration. People share their thoughts and ideas in a non-judgmental, open environment. The aim is to encourage creativity and generate a broad range of views of a problem. Brainstorming is effective because it allows people to build on each other's ideas and come up with innovative solutions that they may not have thought of individually.

- Elimination is a problem-solving technique that involves systematically eliminating variables or options in order to arrive at a solution. This technique is commonly used in mathematics, science, and engineering.

- Critical thinking is the intellectually disciplined process of conceptualizing, applying, analyzing, synthesizing, and/or evaluating information gathered from or generated by observation, experience, reflection, reasoning, or communication as a guide to theory and action. It encourages skeptical reflection and expects you to question everything – e.g., why do you think this? What is the source? What is opinion/conjecture and what is fact? You are objective, not easily convinced or fooled.

- Root cause analysis tries to identify the underlying causes of a problem or issue. It is often used in quality control and process improvement initiatives. The process involves asking "why" questions until the root cause is identified, then steps can be taken to address it and prevent similar issues from arising in the future.

- Trial and error involve experimenting with different solutions until the best one is found by analyzing and implementing ideas and evaluating their effectiveness. Individuals or teams try solutions until the problem is solved.

- The Five Ws. and an H approach are often mentioned in journalism research and police investigations. What is the idea or problem and what do you want to achieve? Why is it a problem or important and why do it? Whose problem is it and who is involved and affected? When did it occur? Start/ finish / duration. Where did or does it happen - inputs, constraints, places, resources, facilities, equipment, and How was it (will it be) done? Each of the Hows can be broken down into smaller (more detailed) Whats.

- Systems thinking involves imagining or picturing problem situations as complex systems and trying to analyze how their notional parts interact and influence each other. It takes a holistic approach to problem-solving, in context, rather than focusing on individual components. The system can include people, processes, structures, technologies, and more. Systems thinking recognizes that changes in one part of a system can have ripple effects throughout the entire system and that the system as a whole is greater than the sum of its individual parts.

- Mind mapping is a visual technique used to organize and represent information. It involves creating a diagram or "map" with thoughts that explode out from a central idea or concept. It can help to capture thoughts, ideas, and information in a creative way, stimulating both logical and creative hemispheres of the brain and allowing for better comprehension, analysis, and synthesis of complex concepts. The central idea or topic can be a single word or a short phrase that represents the main theme or focus. Branches radiate outward and each subtopic can branch out further into details and related ideas. Mind maps often use visual elements such as colors, symbols, icons, and images to enhance the big picture. Visualizing information helps the brain make connections and associations between different ideas.

Unlike traditional linear, note-taking methods, mind maps allow for the exploration of ideas in a less restrictive way, encouraging brainstorming and generating new insights. They provide a good overview of a topic, making issues more manageable and easier to understand. They help identify relationships, hierarchies, and connections between different concepts. They can stimulate creative thinking and problem-solving by encouraging the generation of new ideas and alternative perspectives and can be used as collaborative tools in group discussions and brainstorming sessions.

- *Lateral thinking is a term coined by Edward de Bono. It refers to the use of creative and non-traditional methods to answer and deal with problems that are difficult to solve using conventional thinking. Lateral thinking often requires people to have a willingness to be unconventional, to enjoy being different, to approach a problem from different angles, to recognize and try to eliminate assumptions, to shift their perspective and to consider situations in a different way than normal.

While it can be a powerful tool for generating innovative ideas, there are also some challenges and limitations associated with lateral thinking. It can take more time than traditional problem-solving methods, as it often involves exploring many different avenues and possibilities. It is less structured than traditional problem-solving methods, which can lead to difficulties in prioritizing and implementing ideas. It relies heavily on creativity, which can be challenging for people who do not consider themselves naturally creative or who work in fields that are not typically associated with creativity. It can sometimes generate ideas that are interesting but not practical or feasible. It can be influenced by cultural and contextual factors, which may limit the range of possibilities that individuals can consider. It requires critical evaluation of ideas to determine their potential impact. It can be difficult to measure the success of lateral thinking efforts, as the outcomes may be subjective and difficult to quantify.

- Tables and Matrices can be useful devices for organizing and visualizing apparently complex information. Their row and column structure helps to arrange data and build a clearer picture of a situation. They can highlight trends and patterns. They are especially valuable when we are faced with complicated and varied data as they help to categorize and arrange important facts.

HOW TO ANSWER RIDDLES, PUZZLES AND LATERAL THINKING QUESTIONS

Here are some steps that can help you solve lateral thinking questions, mysteries, riddles, logic puzzles, and brain teasers:

1. **Read the question carefully** to appreciate what's being asked (and what is missing). Take note of any key information, such as numbers or details, and try to visualize the problem in your mind.

2. **Redefine, examine and explain** the question in a different way. Before you can solve a problem, you need to understand it. Take time to describe the problem or question carefully, evaluate the evidence, identify the key issues that need to be addressed and what you are trying to solve.

3. **Undo it**: Break it down into smaller parts. Look for clues that can help you simplify the problem and identify a starting point.

4. **Daydream**: Allow your imagination lots of freedom, explore hunches. Be inquisitive, curious and open-minded.

5. **Challenge assumptions,** and bias questions, gut reactions and preconceived ideas. Try not to jump to conclusions. Identify the assumptions that underlie the problem and examine them critically. Discern fact from opinion. Ask yourself if these apparent truths are really true and whether there might be alternative explanations or approaches.

11

6. **Use logic and deduction**: Many puzzles and riddles require logical reasoning. Try to eliminate poor answers and narrow down the possibilities. Use what you know and apply it to what you don't know.

7. **Look for patterns, relationships and constraints**: Problem-solving often involves finding patterns or connections that are not immediately obvious. Look for similarities or differences between seemingly unrelated things.

8. **Think outside the box**: Sometimes, the answer is not obvious and requires creative leaps of thinking. Try to approach the problem from different perspectives, think about how the pieces can fit in different ways.

9. **Generate alternative solutions**: Explore different possibilities. Come up with as many ideas as you can, no matter how unconventional or silly they may seem. Don't censor yourself – generate many potential solutions.

10. **Collaborate**: puzzles can be fun to solve with other people. Try brainstorming and working with someone else, bounce ideas off each other. Two or three minds are better than one.

11. **Evaluate solutions**: once you have some potential solutions, evaluate them carefully. Look at the pros and cons of each and consider their potential outcomes. Be open to combining different solutions or modifying them to better suit the problem.

12. **Implement ideas**: when you have identified a viable solution, put it into action as it were, try it for size. Make a plan and execute it, keeping in mind any potential obstacles that may arise. Be prepared to adapt your plan as needed and remain flexible in your approach.

13. **Reflect on the process**: consider what you learned, what worked well, and what could have been done differently. Use this knowledge to improve your lateral thinking skills for problems you encounter in the future.

CONCLUSION TO THE INTRODUCTION

In conclusion, brainstorming, logical reasoning and lateral thinking are essential skills for problem-solving in today's complex and rapidly changing world. By following these steps, you can develop your abilities and become more adept at finding innovative solutions to challenging problems. Teach your brain to think creatively. Try to be open-minded, curious, and persistent, and don't be afraid to use new approaches and ideas. Try different methods individually or in combination, don't get discouraged if you cannot solve a problem right away!

Facebook = 600 Puzzles

Email = info@middlepartacademy.com

EASY, FUN, STARTER QUESTIONS

1. Imagine you are trapped in a very dark room that has no doors – how would you get out?

2. Say these answers out loud:

- How do you pronounce the word: S I L K?

- The stripe of stars across the night sky is called "The _____ Way".

- Yogurt is fermented _____?.

- What do cows drink _____?

3. Some months have 31 days, some have 30 days, which month has 28 days?

4. If a red-house is made of red bricks and a white-house is made of white bricks, what is a green-house made of?

5. John's mother has 5 children, one is called Zara, one is called Zere, one is called Zigi, and one is called Zoro. What is the fifth one called?

6. Roughly, how many grooves would you estimate that there are in the average long-playing vinyl record?

7. How long is the answer to this question?

8. You see a man walking in a strange, ungainly, awkward way on the pavement sidewalk – as if he is drunk or injured – but he starts to walk normally when he enters a park. What do you think is the reason for this?

9. A daddy bull drinks 6 gallons of water a day and a baby bull drinks 2 gallons. How much will a mummy bull drink?

10. There are three apples; if you take away two, how many apples do you have?

11. How can you divide 2 Neapolitan pizzas equally among 3 people?

12. Which is heavier: a ton of stones or a ton of feathers?

13. Name (in English) three consecutive days without using the words Monday, Wednesday or Saturday.

14. It looked like there had been a terrible accident – worse than those that occur sometimes on a busy road in very foggy weather. Numerous vehicles, including a tractor, a fire engine, an army tank and at least a dozen cars, were in the pile. Some were upside down, some were buried under others, yet no one was injured. How did this happen?

15. What gets wetter as it dries?

16. A man wearing a mask walked hurriedly into a bank in Cape Town, approached the counter and handed over a piece of paper to the cashier. He took out a large carrier bag and started stuffing cash into it. The security guard became suspicious and came over to see what was going on but the cashier sent him away and the man left the bank without being detained. What was happening?

17. If you drive a bus with 32 people on board from Edinburgh to London and drop off 3 people at each of 6 stops and pick up 4 people at half the stops, when you arrive in London 9 hours later, how old is the driver?

18. How many birthdays do cats have?

19. A man walks into a bar and asks for a glass of water. The bartender pulls out a shotgun, points it at him and shouts threateningly. The man says, "*Thank you*," and walks out. Why did the man thank the bartender?

20. The speed of sound in air is about 740 miles per hour (MPH). If a fire engine is driving towards you at 60 MPH with its siren on, at what speed is the sound of the siren approaching you?

21. What is it that, the more you take, the more you leave behind?

22. A man knows that he won a big prize in the lottery 2 weeks ago but has not left his job, made any attempt to go home or claim the prize – why?

23. A rifle has been set up very carefully, with a spirit level, so that it sits horizontally 6 feet above the ground. Suppose that, at the moment it is fired, another bullet is dropped from the same height (6 feet). Ignoring frictional effects and the curvature of the earth, which bullet will hit the ground first?

24. This sentence contains two misstakes. How many errors does it have?

25. You arrive late at night at your friend's off-grid cabin, deep in the woods. You only brought one match with you. Which do you light first, the newspaper, the oil lamp, the candle, or the fire?

26. Harold was killed instantly when he fell asleep while driving at 70MPH and crashed into six vehicles coming the other way. Although all the vehicles were badly damaged, only one other person was hurt or needed treatment – why?

27. Someone has put one of your rings into an empty bottle and inserted a cork into the neck. How can you remove the ring without removing the cork or breaking the bottle?

28. A little girl named Lucy, who loved her white pet mouse very much, was sad to see it did not look well one day. It had not eaten the food she left for it and it was hardly moving. She carried it gently to the local pet shop, where she bought all her pet food, and asked nice Mr. Lyon, the owner, if he had any medicine to cure the mouse. Mr. Lyon said *"Yes of course – I have some in the pet hospital – I'll just be a minute."* He carried the little mouse to a room at the back of the shop and when he returned, the mouse looked much better. Lucy was really happy. How did Mr. Lyon achieve this apparently miraculous recovery?

---

29. What are you bound to find in the middle of Toronto?

---

30. A hotel owner left a £50 note behind the bar to pay the plumber for some work he was doing before the hotel was opened for the new season. The £50 note disappeared but the plumber complained he had not been paid. The owner interviewed the 3 other people in the hotel at the time. The cook said he saw the note and worried that it might blow away so he put a book over it. The owner checked – there was a book behind the bar, but there was nothing under it. He asked the janitor who said yes, he had seen the note and thought it would be better to hide it inside the book. The owner checked again but found nothing inside the book. The waiter said he saw the note poking out of the book so he hid it behind the hardback dustcover. The owner knew who the thief was – can you guess why?

---

31. What must you keep after giving it to someone?

32. A sports car was driven at breakneck speed through a village, it hit two other cars, narrowly missed a pedestrian and crashed into a wall. The incident was caught on camera and there were lots of witnesses but despite that, the driver was not prosecuted – why not?

33. What is black when you buy it, red when you use it, and grey when you have finished with it?

34. How did a horse that was tied to a 10-foot long rope reach a pile of hay 20 feet away?

35. A wealthy film star lives an ostentatious life in an expensive mansion near a beach and employs several staff to look after him. He is not well-liked; rumors abound that he is a bully and treats his staff badly. At about 9:00 am one Sunday morning, his wife got up and found his dead body in the study. It looked like he had been clubbed to death. The police determined that the murder had happened between 8:00 am and 8:30 am. They interviewed everyone in the house. Asking them what they had been doing at that time. His wife was asleep, the gardener was pruning roses, the chef was preparing breakfast, his personal assistant was walking down the long driveway to get the mail / post, the butler was cleaning the sitting room, and the laundry person was ironing shirts. Who did the police suspect?

36. What vehicle has no wings but can travel over water and land, hardly touching either?

37. If you're running in a race and you pass the person in second place, what place are you in?

38. You meet a man who tells you that he has married 25 women; why was he allowed to do this?

39. What has 13 hearts but no other organs?

40. On his way home from an all-day wine tasting session, a professional sommelier was caught speeding. He was relieved to pass the breathalyzer test but then he knew he would. Why was he so confident?

41. Take away a letter from this odd number and it becomes even. What number?

42. A woman in a café, who had been eating a bowl of consommé soup with a spoon, calls the waitress over and asks for a straw – she says she wants to use the straw to finish eating the soup – why?

---

43. A pilot was demonstrating how to perform a loop and barrel roll when he lost control and crashed. Why was no one injured?

---

44. The police were not especially surprised to find the body of a well-known gangster slumped over in his car; he had a lot of enemies. It looked like he had been shot at close range an hour or two earlier in the evening. What did surprise the police was that, at the time, the car had been surrounded by other cars and people yet no one heard the shots or raised the alarm. How come?

---

45. If two's company, and three's a crowd, what are four and five?

---

46. A little girl is walking beside her mum, holding hands and paying attention to her surroundings, suddenly she breaks away and runs towards a lion. Her mum calls her back but is not frightened – why not?

---

47. Ten friends have rented a big house in the country. One is fishing; one is riding a bike; one is doing the washing up; one is chopping vegetables; one has gone for a walk; one is reading a book; one is playing tennis; one is answering emails; one is asleep. Any idea what the tenth person is doing?

48. A woman, standing at a bus stop, was horrified when a man, driving a scooter, stopped beside her, grabbed her handbag and drove off. She described the whole incident clearly to the police and 2 witnesses gave statements. Based on her description, the police told her they knew who to look for – a local man was famous for this type of crime – they arrested him and brought him to court. Why did the judge throw the case out?

49. A man accused of being a spy is told, *"Tell a lie and you will be hung; tell the truth and you will be shot."* What did he say to try to save himself?

50. A husband teased his wife telling her that, on his way home, he had been subjected to a sudden violent storm that thrashed and soaked the car for a few minutes and was gone as suddenly as it began. What was he talking about?

Logic

51. Your brother has installed a clever immobilizer in his car. It consists of 3 switches, side by side, that can each be set: Up, Down, or Middle. He explains that if you do not set the switches into the correct positions before you start the car, the system will lock for 10 minutes. He tells you that, to start the car, the number of switches in the Up position must be the same as the number in the Down position, that a Down and an Up cannot be next to each other, that any switch set to Middle cannot have another switch set to Middle beside it and that the first switch should be Up.

52. Why are 1984 bottles of Jura whiskey more valuable than 1939 bottles of Jura whiskey?

53. Your friend takes 4 cards from a deck of playing cards and places them face down on the table in front of you. She tells you that there is a 7, an 8, a 9 and a 10 and that there is a club, a heart, a diamond and a spade. She gives you some guidelines and challenges you to figure out the order the cards have been placed in. You are told that: a) neither of the two middle cards is a club, b) if you add the two middle cards together, you get an even number, c) the spade is to the left of the heart, d) the 8 is between two black cards, e) the club is not next to the 7 but it is to the right of it. Can you work out the numerical and suit order of the cards?

54. How could you throw a ball as hard as you can, make it stop, and return to you without hitting anything and with nothing attached to it?

55. What are the next two letters in the following series and why? WATNTLITFS _ _

56. You have made it through to the last and final round of a competition to win a car. One question is all that stands in your way. If you answer it correctly, you win the new car, get it wrong and you walk away with nothing. You face 2 identical garages; the car is parked in one of them. Two people (guards) stand in front of the garages, a man and a woman. You are told that one of these people always tells the truth and the other always lies. They both know where the car is. You have to come up with a question that will tell you where the car is; you can only ask one of the guards one question. What is that single question?

57. Mary has 8 or more sons. Mary has less than 8 sons. Mary has at least 1 son. If only one of these statements is true, how many sons does Mary have?

58. You own a small shop. Micky, the owner of the shop next door warns you that they have just found a counterfeit £20 note in today's takings. Micky figured out who left the fake note and when he describes this woman, you realize she bought something from you as well. Micky lends you a useful machine he rented from the bank that can check for fake notes. The machine has 3 slots; you can use as many of these as you like. The slots shine very bright light through a stack of notes and clever software detects if any of the notes in that pile are fakes. An alarm buzzer sounds and a red-light flashes over the slot with a fake note if one is found. You have received fifteen £20 notes so far today. You will be charged £1 every time you use the machine. What is the least number of times you need to use it?

---

59. You are traveling with 2 young sheep and a large hungry dog. You need to cross a river. There is a small canoe on the bank. You know it can only carry you and one animal at a time. You do not want to leave a sheep alone with the dog. How can you get them all over to the other side of the river?

---

60. When you reach the river the next time, you are traveling with a leopard, a goat, and a bale of hay. The canoe can only carry you and one other. If you leave them, the leopard will eat the goat and the goat will eat the hay. How do you get them all across safely?

---

61. You are reading a novel about an international cat burglar who leaves notes everywhere s/he goes that taunt authorities and say: "*Catch me if you can*". The book invites you, the reader, to be a detective and figure out what is going to happen next as the chapters roll on. The thief steals gold and silver coins and jewels and each chapter tells the story of one of the complicated and ingenious thefts. Chapter 1 began with a theft from a billionaire's house in Canada; then the burglar moved to Europe. Chapter 2's crime occurred in an expensive jewel shop in Austria chapter 3 from a bazaar in Turkey; chapter 4 was from a coin collector in Cyprus and chapter 5 from an art gallery in Hungary, then a Monaco casino, then a souk in Egypt then an emporium in Israel, then a museum in Finland. Where will the thief strike next?

---

62. You are a park warden. Someone has tied a vicious dog to a tree with a long rope. The dog is lunging at anyone who comes within 20 feet of the tree. People are justifiably scared. You do not want to go too near to the dog but you want to restrict its movement a bit until a dog catcher arrives. What can you do?

---

63. A lawyer announced the last will and testament of a man who had two sons. It stated that the old man wanted to leave everything to the cleverest son. To decide which of the two to leave his fortune to, he had set up a challenge. The lawyer explained that each son was to be given £1,000 to spend on a bicycle and that whichever son crossed the finish line last was the winner. They could buy any bike they liked, new or second-hand, do as much work to it as they liked (within the budget) and practice or train any way they wanted to. After a month, not sure what to do, they both went to see their uncle for advice. Within minutes they rushed out of their uncle's house, jumped onto the bikes and raced to the finish line as fast as they could. What advice did their uncle give?

---

64. You light a small fire on a beach at one end of a long thin island that is about 5 kilometers long and 100 meters wide. The island is covered in vegetation that is very dry from a long drought. You are the only person on the island. Suddenly a spark from your fire ignites the nearby vegetation. A wind is fanning the flames and you realize the fire will burn progressively down the whole island, destroying everything in its path within a few hours. The island has no other beach, only sheer cliffs and the sea is infested with sharks. What can you do to avoid being burnt?

---

65. There are two plastic jugs filled with water. How could you put all of this water into a barrel and still tell which water came from which jug?

---

66. A middle-aged woman heard someone knocking on her hotel room door in the middle of the day. She opened the door warily, just enough to see the man standing in the corridor. She asked him what he wanted. He seemed surprised to see her and said "*Apologies madam, I thought this was my room*". The woman immediately slammed the door shut and phoned hotel reception. Why was she so suspicious?

---

67. A hospital became busier after the seat-belt wearing law was introduced; why?

---

68. People died because a man overslept and was late doing his job. He lived on his own, in a building on the coast, and was responsible for performing one important task every day. What was his job?

69. A husband and wife were on holiday exploring the great vineyards of Bordeaux in France. Soon after leaving the village, they had stayed the previous night in, they came to a crossroads. The crossroads signpost used to point to 4 different places but it had fallen over. How did they work out which was the way to the next vineyard they wanted to visit?

70. Frank had a plan to go to a casino, buy lots of colorful gaming chips with cash, play Blackjack for about 20 minutes, cash in his chips and leave. Why did he want to leave so quickly and what is wrong with this plan?

71. A man was killed because he forgot to bring a piece of furniture to work. Why?

72. Michael and his wife have a car that seats a maximum of 4 people. He drives Lizzy to work every day and drops his 3 children off at school on the way. How does he fit them all in the car?

73. A lorry driver has discovered, just too late, that his truck is slightly too high to fit under a bridge. Luckily, he was going quite slowly, so neither the truck nor the bridge was badly damaged. It looks like the truck is only about one inch too high to pass under. A young boy comes along and makes a suggestion and saves the day. What was the suggestion?

74. On a walk in the highlands, Kate and Rob suddenly found themselves on the opposite side of a river to their dog Lukka. The river was about 20 feet wide. Kate called *"Come on Lukka"* and the brave little terrier, who does not like swimming, crossed the river and ran to her to be congratulated. Somehow, he did not get wet – why? (There is no bridge nearby).

75. Many of the visitors to a pretty Alpine village were amused and entertained by the person who called himself the village idiot. When he was offered a choice of a shiny £1 coin or an old £10 note, he always chose the coin. Why?

76. You at a dinner party. The meal is over and someone suggests you all play a game. You tell the other 5 people you know a fun challenge. You take a pack of ordinary playing cards, shuffle them and place them face down. You then cover the pile with your left hand and slide a joker card into this pile. The other people cannot see where you put it. You explain that one by one, each person (apart from you) must turn the top card over. The person who turns over the joker loses. If the card they turn is not a joker they (alone) can sneak a look at the next 3 cards in the pile, at which point they can choose to: a) turn over the topmost of these three cards, b) turn over two of these cards c) turn over all three cards or d) turn over none of the cards. If / when someone sees the joker, they cannot say anything. Each player has the option (just before they turn a card over) to pass their turn on to you, but this option is only available once in the game. The challenge is to see if they can come up with a plan to work together to defeat you. Once the game starts, they cannot speak or make any gestures to each other. What is their best strategy?

77. Your friend Sharon tells you a story. She shares an apartment with 3 others, one of whom loves pistachio nuts. This person always keeps a big tin full of pistachios so he can grab a handful whenever he likes. Sharon admits she has started to dip into this tin and take some nuts from time to time. The pistachio nut person is becoming suspicious – he has noticed that the nuts seem to be disappearing mysteriously quickly. Sharon asks you if you can think of a clever tactic to stop the nut person suspecting her of all the thefts. Ignoring ethical worries, can you think of a way that might be achieved?

78. On a treasure-hunting trip, you find six ancient gold chains. Each chain is made of just 4 linked rings. You want to link the six short chains together to make one long chain. What is the least number of rings you will need to break or open to do this? (You do not want to add any new rings). P.S. This puzzle might be easier to visualize and solve if you draw a picture or sketch of the problem.

79. A man lives alone in a house 10 miles from the nearest village. The house does not have an electricity supply and he gets water from a nearby stream. He is still trying to adjust to life without his wife; she died a month ago. He is angry with himself one morning when he wakes up and realizes he has forgotten to wind the reliable old grandfather clock up. It was a job his wife had always done. The clock has stopped; it was the only timepiece in the house so he has little idea what the time is. He decides he must walk to the village the next day to find out the time so that he can reset the grandfather clock. How can he do that? The return journey will take hours.

80. It is your birthday. There are 4 envelopes on the table. One of the envelopes has a £10 note in it; the other 3 contain small pieces of paper with smiley faces drawn on them. Each envelope has a message written on it but only one of these messages is true. The first says "the money is in here", the second says "the money is in here", the third says "this envelope contains blank paper" and the fourth says "the money is not in the second envelope". You have one chance to guess which envelope the money is in. Which would you guess?

Assumptions

81. A train makes the same round trip several times, but it does not always stop at stations, no one gets on or off and it only runs on holidays; why?

82. Is it legal for a man to marry his widow's sister?

83. A window cleaner who is cleaning the windows on the 30th floor of an office skyscraper slips when he stands on his tiptoes to reach a corner and falls. He has no cage or safety net below him, yet he is not hurt badly. How did he survive the fall?

84. The queen moved in when a horse jumped over a bishop, dangerously close to the king. In what context does this make sense?

85. A plane carrying 100 British tourists crashed in the Pyrenees on the border between France and Spain. Under international law, where should the survivors be buried?

86. You find a coin dated 153 BC; how old is it and should you hand it over to a museum?

87. A man lies dead between two small collapsed piles of bricks. He has a beetle on his head. How did he die?

88. Stan ran away from home as fast as he could. Why was a man wearing a mask waiting for him and blocking his path when he tried to come home?

89. You have two buckets of water; the water in the first bucket is 30 degrees centigrade, the water in the other bucket is 30 degrees Fahrenheit. If you drop a small coin into each which will reach the bottom first?

90. A man staggered out of a nightclub, fell over, got to his feet in a drunken way and fumbled with his keys as he tried to open his car. Two policemen, who had been sitting in their police car in the car park, watched as he drove away. They chased after him with their blue lights flashing and soon pulled him over. They were surprised when the breathalyzer test was negative so they asked him to do it again. It was negative once more. Puzzled, they let him go. If he was not drunk, why did he appear so?

91. Two planes are flying towards each other across the Atlantic. The one from New York is flying at 600 MPH, the one from Lisbon is flying at 500 MPH. When the 2 planes meet which will be closer to Lisbon?

92. You hear that many young children are being brought to be interrogated by an old man in a cave; why?

93. Two men who have known each other for a long time and recently returned home from a lengthy stay abroad meet at a special seafood restaurant. One of them orders a dish of turtle meat. He is horrified as soon as he tastes it. He stands up and shouts at the other man before storming off. He goes to the nearest church to pray and confess. Can you think of any circumstances that make sense of this story?

94. A large room is occupied by a King, a Queen, and two twins. Although they are visited and dressed and undressed quite often, they never move. Explain?

95. Two golfers, Jim and Alec, are playing a game. They each scored 30 when Jim mistimes his swing and hits a bad shot. This mistake adds 10 points to Alec's score. Soon after that, Alec hits a superb shot and wins the game. Can you explain this apparently nonsensical situation?

96. A woman stops her car at a hotel and is told she is bankrupt. Why?

97. You have to enter one of three rooms: the first has a fire that is raging out of control, the second has a tiger that has not eaten for a year and the third has a deadly assassin with a sharp knife – which room would you choose?

98. A father and his son are driving back from a football game when a truck crashes into them, injuring them both badly. They are rushed to the hospital but the surgeon on duty does not want to operate on them and calls in another surgeon instead – why?

99. A bright red car and a shiny black car crash into each other head-on, causing a lot of damage to both cars. The police are called and although a dead man is found in one of the cars, they only take a few notes and do not charge anyone with manslaughter. Why?

100. What happened in Oldenburg on the 31st June, 1942?

101. It was a lovely, warm, sunny day so Margaret took Sally, her 4-year-old, to the beach. Soon after they got there, a big dog saw them and started to run towards Sally. Why was Margaret not concerned by this?

---

102. Mr. Burton is a philanthropist; he has been buying food and sending it to those in need in Africa for over 10 years. Eventually, he will become a millionaire; how will he manage to do that?

---

103. A small square house, far from civilization, is unusual because all 4 sides face south. Looking out of one of the windows, you see a bear; what color is it?

---

104. A car, driven far too fast, down a narrow back street, without its headlights on, screeched to a halt just before it crashed into a ninja who was sneaking down the street, dressed from head to toe in black (black shoes, socks, trousers, coat, gloves and head mask) when all the overhead street lights were off. How did the young driver see the ninja?

---

105. A crowd of people watched a man approach a woman he had never met before and give her a long kiss. It happened outdoors, on a crowded street, in broad daylight; no words were exchanged between them, she did not try to stop him, and they were not actors in a movie. After it was over, everyone watching applauded. Can you explain?

106. I make a habit of destroying fingerprints at the local police station. Why and who am I?

107. Arthur lives in a nice apartment in Charleston. Last week, while the person he lives with had popped out to get some milk, two men burst into the apartment and, ignoring Arthur, took the TV and a laptop computer. Arthur had never seen the men before, and they had no legal right to remove the equipment, yet he did nothing to stop them. In fact, he didn't even act surprised by their behavior. Why not?

108. When he left home, Harry was wearing a disguise and a mask and carrying an empty sack. He returned 2 hours later with a full sack and went to bed. Harry is not a burglar, so what is he?

109. When you visit the local primary school, the headmistress asks if you would like to hear about one of the tests the kids are given when they start at the school. *"Yes"* you say, *"How does it go?" "Well"* says the headmistress *"We half fill a bathtub with water and then offer each child a big spoon, a teacup and a jug and ask them to empty the bathtub."* What do the cleverest ones do?

110. A girl who was a learner driver and had not passed her driving test went the wrong way down a one-way street but did not break the law. How come?

TRIVIA

---

111. Which country has a wife-carrying race and what is the winner's prize?

---

112. How long do elephant pregnancies last?

---

113. How many insects and spiders might one person eat, in the course of an average lifetime, while sleeping?

---

114. Which country consumes the most chocolate per person?

---

115. How long was the longest wedding veil ever created?

---

116. What did "Gardyloo" mean?

---

117. Which sport has been played on the moon?

118. Ancient Romans boiled vinegar and goat dung to make what?

119. A 73-year-old bottle of French Burgundy became the most expensive bottle of wine ever sold at auction in 2018. How much was the winning bid?

120. Who was the first woman to win a Nobel Prize?

121. What is the name of the hottest chili pepper?

122. From where to where is the shortest commercial flight in the world?

123. Which country banned hula hoops?

124. Apart from humans, do any other animals have fingerprints?

125. Which country features a shipwreck on its national flag?

126. What are the odds of getting a royal flush (Ace, King, Queen, Jack,10 of the same suit) in poker?

127. What did someone purchase with 10,000 Bitcoins (now worth around $250,000,000) on May, the 22nd, 2010?

128. How many moons does Saturn have?

129. Which monarch made Valentine's Day a holiday in 1537?

130. In Texas, it is illegal to do what when one is near a dead person?

131. How long do Greenland sharks live?

132. What is the world hot dog eating record – number and time?

133. How do lobsters communicate?

134. Which country has the oldest surviving working hotel and how old is it?

135. What color is hippopotamus milk?

136. How much of their lives does the average driver wait at traffic lights?

137. What age was Mary Shelley when she wrote Frankenstein?

138. What is the percentage of American dollar bills that have residues of cocaine?

139. How much bamboo does a giant panda eat in a year?

140. Roughly how many grapes go into a bottle of wine?

141. Who named the Pacific Ocean?

142. How many languages are written from right to left?

143. Which company was the first to trademark its service uniforms in the U.S.A?

144. How much more powerful is a dog's sense of smell than a human's?

145. What was Alfred Hitchcock afraid of?

146. How much does hair grow per year, on average, in inches (or centimeters)?

147. Which is the most poisonous vertebrate in the world, said to be more toxic than cyanide, that is regarded by some in Japan as a gourmet delicacy?

148. What is the purpose of human "goosebumps"?

149. How many sheets of toilet paper were British soldiers given per day in WW2?

150. What is a flock of crows called?

151. How fast can a tsunami wave travel?

152. If all national flags were square instead of rectangular, which country's flag would look the same whichever of the 4 sides you hung it from?

153. How many mosquitos can a bat eat per night?

154. According to a survey, which fictional character do 25% of Americans believe was a real person?

155. How old is the oldest known living land animal?

156. What are the speed and movement direction of a computer mouse measured in?

157. What is the only food substance that never goes bad?

158. Which famous country and western singing star came 3rd in her own look-alike contest?

159. How many wives and concubines did King Solomon have, reputedly?

160. What were the first ice hockey pucks made of?

161. How many times per minute do we blink?

162. How old is the legend of the Loch Ness monster?

163. What is "Alice in Wonderland syndrome"?

164. Which type of animal are you not allowed to tease in Minnesota?

165. What European country has a national anthem with 158 verses?

166. Hippopotomostrosesquippedaliophobia is the fear of what?

167. Is the total weight of all the ants in the world greater than or less than the total weight of all the humans?

168. What animal cannot stick out its tongue?

169. The first person ever convicted of speeding was going at what speed?

170. Leonardo Da Vinci's painting of the last supper is one of the world's most famous works of art. Why were Jesus's feet cut off the painting in 1652?

171. How many dominos are in a set and how many spots are on all the dominos in a set?

172. How many hearts does an octopus have?

173. What is the coldest temperature ever recorded on Earth?

174. The unicorn is the national animal of which country?

175. What do you call a group of unicorns?

176. Which is larger – an ostrich's brain or its eye?

177. Some ancient chewing gum was discovered in 2007 by an archaeology student in Finland. It is thought to be the oldest piece of chewing gum ever found. How old is it believed to be?

178. What is the women's world record for holding a plank position? Is it over 10 or 30 or 60 or 90 or 120 or 150 or 180 or 210 or 240 or 270 or 300 minutes?

179. What did John Paul Getty, one of the richest men in the world, install in his house?

180. Which is longer on the planet Venus – a year or a day?

181. How many lakes does Canada have: over 100,000; 500,000; 1,000,000; 2,000,000; or 3,000,000?

182. What phrase is thought to be the toughest tongue twister in the English language?

183. How much (as a percentage) of our body's blood and oxygen does our brain use?

184. About 200 countries in the world use the metric system when quantifying and describing measurements such as length or capacity or mass. Name up to 3 countries that do not.

185. Which is the strongest muscle in the human body?

186. Where are 99% of all farmed artichokes grown?

187. Rats can breed and multiply very quickly. How many descendants could two rats have in 20 months?

188. What did the first director of the FBI, J. Edgar Hoover, ban people from walking on?

189. How much of the world's freshwater is held in ice sheets, glaciers, and permanent snow?

190. What was Walt Disney afraid of?

191. Through how many European capital cities does the River Danube flow?

192. Does playing video games make you a better surgeon?

193. What is it illegal for a single woman to do, on Sundays, in Florida?

194. Which 2 countries include the color purple in their national flags?

195. What percentage of the world's population is over 60 years of age?

196. What do giraffes do at night to keep in touch with other members of their herd?

197. Where is the tallest building in the world?

198. It is legal to shoot them, but illegal to do what to bears in Alaska.

199. A Spanish galleon, carrying gold, silver, jewels, and other precious cargo sank near the Florida Keys in 1622. It is listed as one of the most valuable shipwreck treasures ever discovered. What was its estimated value when it was found?

200. How far could medieval archers, with longbows, fire arrows?

201. How many paintings did Vincent van Gogh sell while he was alive?

202. How many bathrooms does London's Buckingham Palace have?

203. What is the largest menu item in the world?

204. In ancient Greece, what were you showing or telling someone by throwing an apple at them?

205. Name 3 cars that have horses on their logos?

206. What is the most common color of toilet paper in France?

207. Name 2 countries that do not allow tattoos.

208. What is the world's fastest bird?

209. How many towels are stolen from Holiday Inns per year in the USA?

210. Which animal's faeces were once used as a contraceptive?

211. What famous geographical feature is about 7 miles from where it started?

212. How many planes have disappeared and never been found?

213. Why do vultures very rarely, if ever, cross the border from southwestern Spain into Portugal?

214. How many different pieces of wood does it take to make a violin?

215. What is illegal in public places in Florida if you are wearing a swimming costume?

216. Finland has more saunas than cars. Why are there so many saunas in Finland?

217. What was the first man-made object to break the sound barrier?

218. Why is it illegal to own just one guinea pig in Switzerland?

219. What was so unusual about the winner of the first Sydney to Melbourne Ultra-marathon?

220. Which movie star has appeared in over 80 films, speaks 5 languages, has undergraduate and Master's degrees in chemical engineering, won a scholarship to MIT, holds the rank of 4th dan black belt in karate and was European champion in 1980–81, and became a bodyguard for Jamaican singer Grace Jones.

PLAYING WITH WORDS

221. What five-letter word becomes shorter when you add two letters to it?

222. What begins with an "e" and contains one letter?

223. Which four-letter word goes after TEA or SHOE and before FROG or HOUSE?

224. What (English) word is pronounced the same if you take away four of its five letters?

225. What is the message contained in the following words: WIECCSR, HDCKRTO, YTHEOHA and DHINSED.

226. Which is the longest one-syllable word in the English language?

227. The first 2 letters of this word indicate male, the first 3 indicate female, the first 4 may be applied to a brave man and the whole word describes a brave woman who we look up to. What is this word?

228. Which is the odd one out and why: Rats, Live, Snug, Trap, Cats, Pans, Keep?

229. What nationalities can you insert before these words to make well-known songs or films or foods or phrases: wood, job, falcon, yogurt, courage, man o'war, heels, chef, guards, fly, connection, shepherd, stew, delight.

230. Which 5 letter word do almost all Oxford University graduates pronounce wrong?

231. What do the following have in common: A H I M O T U V W X Y?

232. Name nine human body parts that are only 3 letters long.

233. What completes the list; sore, keel, cosh mark?

234. There are only 2 English words that start and end with the letters "he", many people would say that they are connected; what are they?

235. What animals can you add to make the following words make sense: af_oon, appr_imate, mead_ark, bil_aire, bene_nt, ver_im, si_ure, _orker, mi_ave, ex_ble, cont_e?

236. Madam, level, civic, and noon are all similar in a way. Name one more word that conforms to this type.

237. What 3 letter English verb changes from present to past tense when you rearrange the letters?

238. Can you add one letter to the beginning of each of these words to make them countries and then suggest a 6-letter girl's name to add to this list: had, inland, ran, man, pain?

239. How many upper-case words look the same backwards and upside down (if all their letters are typed as capital letters)?

240. Are there any words that look the same backwards and upside down, not using capital letters?

241. What interesting characteristics do these words share: bad, ball, dan, mass, pat, tan?

242. A common English word has 4 very different meanings as you remove and alter its letters. With 5 letters, it is something you can eat, take the first letter away and it becomes a form of energy, take the next letter away and you need to do this to live, scramble the remaining 3 letters and you can drink it. What is this 5-letter word?

243. Which is the only English word that ends in the letters "mt".

244. A 9 letter English word is extraordinary because you can remove letters from it, one by one, and it goes on being meaningful words. What are the 9, 8, 7, 6, 5, 4, 3, 2, and 1 letter words?

245. Can you make three words from the following two words: "deer throws"?

246. What is the longest word in the English language with only one vowel?

247. Here are 4 short phrases and sentences. The 4th is unfinished, can you find the last 2 words? 1) astronomers are moon starters; 2) the Statue of Liberty was built to stay free; 3) be silent and listen; 4) the eyes _____ _____.

248. Name 3 English language words that end in "dous".

249. Which word contains the following letters: PRTGS?

250. What is strangely unusual and quite remarkable about the following words: revive, banana, grammar, voodoo, assess, potato, dresser, uneven?

RIDDLES

251. What is full of holes but holds a lot of water?

252. Although my host finds me to be a growing irritation, I cannot be evicted until and unless, one day, I am taken and sold. What am I?

253. What belongs to you but is used by others more than you?

254. Your Grandma tells you that, years ago, she shot her husband, held him down in a bath of liquid for 5 minutes, and then hung him. But that evening, they both went out and enjoyed a wonderful night out together. How could this be?

255. What is it that, given one, you will have either two or none?

256. I am taller when I am young and shorter when I am older; what am I?

257. What can fill a room without taking up any space?

258. What is harder to catch the faster you run?

259. The day before two days after the day before tomorrow is Friday. What day is it today?

260. Richard went into a shop, pointed and asked *"How much does it cost for one?"* The assistant replied *"£2 sir"*. Richard said *"How much for 10?"* The assistant replied *"£4 sir"*. Next Richard asked *"How much for 100?"* and the reply was *"£6"*. What is Richard buying?

261. What do you throw out when you want to use it but bring in when you don't want to use it?

262. What runs but never walks, has a bed but never sleeps, and has a mouth but never speaks?

263. If you look for me, whether you are high or low, you may be able to see me anywhere in the world. You can move towards me but I am always far away, somewhere amid land or sea and sky. What am I?

264. What is used in most sports that (usually) has four holes in it?

265. What kind of ring is square?

266. Take me out and scratch my head; I am now black but once was red. What am I?

267. Carbon dioxide + vinegar + carbolic acid - aspirin = What

268. What kind of coat is wet when you put it on?

269. A woman had two sons who were born on the same day of the same year, but they were not twins. How could this be true?

270. What can be bigger than you but does not weigh anything?

271. What starts with T, ends in T and has T in it?

272. Everyone needs it and although it is often given, people may not take it. What is it?

273. He makes shoes using all four elements, fire, water, air and earth, but not leather. Most of his customers take two pairs. Who is he?

274. What do the following sentences have in common and what is unique about the second one? "The quick brown fox jumps over the lazy dog." "Jackdaws love my big sphinx of quartz".

275. Which ball sport can also be eaten?

276. When you have me, you often feel like sharing me, but if you share me, I no longer exist. What am I?

277. How many hands does the Big Ben clock in London have?

278. What has 4 fingers and a thumb but is not alive?

279. Smile at me and I'll smile back, but drop me and I'll surely crack. What am I?

280. What is a planet and a god and a measure of heat?

281. Going forward, I weigh a ton but backwards I do not. What am I?

282. Five things can be found in a tennis court that all authors need. What are they?

283. How do you share 25 apples among 19 people so that they all get equal amounts?

284. I can be hot, bad, ill, and short. What am I?

285. What has branches but no fruit, trunk, or leaves?

286. A rebus is a riddle or puzzle made up of letters, pictures, and symbols whose names sound like the syllables and words of a phrase or sentence. For example, "Ci ii" represents "See eye to eye." What word or phrase does the following rebus represent: O_ER_T_O_?

---

287. What can run all around a garden but never move?

---

288. Whether you are left or right-handed, what can you hold in your right hand that you cannot hold in your left hand?

---

289. What can you do to buttons, shopping trolleys, and your luck?

---

290. How can a man shave several times a day and have a long beard?

---

291. What cannot talk but calls back if we shout?

---

292. Name a word that is a fruit, a team, and a bird?

---

293. What can be sliced but stay whole, be driven without wheels, be cut without leaving a scar and be chipped without frying?

294. What falls but never breaks and what breaks but never falls?

295. It is shorter than the rest, but you might show it when pleased or when you need a lift. What is it?

296. Two in front, two behind, and one in the middle; how many are there?

297. What is small, round, tossed up and served at a table for 2 or 4 people?

298. The maker does not need it, the buyer does not use it and the user uses it without knowing. What is it?

299. What occurs once in a minute, twice in a moment, and never in a thousand years?

300. In which sport do losers move forwards and winners move backwards?

Numbers

301. How can the following formula ever be correct? 6 x 6 = 18

302. An old steam locomotive travels at 30 kilometres per hour through a tunnel. If the length of the tunnel is half a kilometre, how long will it take from the time the train enters the tunnel to time it reappears at the other end of the tunnel?

303. Why is the number 8549176320 so special?

304. A snail starts to climb up the inside of a well from the bottom. The well is 30 feet deep. Each day it climbs 3 feet, but each night it slips back 2 feet. How many days will it take to reach the top?

305. You have been metal detecting and found 8 silver coins, they look very similar and you think that they are all identical weights except one which might be a bit heavier than the others. Using a balance scale, how can you work out which is the heavy one in just 2 weighings?

306. Which 3 numbers give the same result whether you add them or multiply them?

307. You have 2 fuse strings. One is rated to burn for 6 minutes, the other for 2 minutes. A friend challenges you to think of a way that you could measure 4 minutes just using these fuses? You are not allowed to cut or bend them.

308. In 5 year's time, I will be 3 times as old as I was 3 years ago. How old am I now?

309. What is interesting about these two phrases: "eleven plus two" = "twelve plus one"?

310. Why can you add 5 to 6 and get 11 but add 7 to 6 and get 1?

311. You want to cut a rope that is 40 meters long into 1-meter sections. If it takes 2 seconds to cut off one-meter length, how long will it take to produce all the pieces?

312. Is this code for the start of a famous number: CADAEIBFEC?

313. If 2 times 2 = 4, what does 2 to the power of 2 times 2 plus two with 2 divided by 2 subtracted from it? Hint: (2^(2*2+2))-2/2.

314. Your uncle passed away recently. He split the money in his bank account 4 ways. He left you half of the money and half of that to his godson. He left an old friend a sixth of the money and gave £1,000 to charity. How much money did he leave altogether?

315. How much earth is in a hole 4 feet long, by 3 feet wide by 2 feet deep?

316. As I was going to St. Ives, I met a man with seven wives; each wife had seven sacks, each sack had seven chickens, each chicken had seven baby chicks. Chicks, hens, sacks and wives, how many were going to St. Ives?

317. You have 1,000 small wooden cubes and stack them so that they form a larger cube = 10 by 10 by 10. How many are left in the cube if you remove 1 layer of cubes?

318. If 5 sewing machinists can make 5 T-shirts in 5 minutes, how many minutes will it take 100 sewing machinists to make 100 T-shirts?

319. You apply for a new job and one of the tests you are given asks you to figure out what the # symbol in the following equations means. 8#5 = 31340; 9#3 = 51227; 10#9 = 11990. So what does 7#6 = ?

320. When my daughter was 9, her little brother was a third of her age. She is now 25; what age is her little brother?

321. A bag contains exactly 60 ping pong balls of 3 different colors. There are four times as many red balls as green and six more blue balls than green balls. How many balls of each color are there?

322. In a group of 23 people, what is the chance that two of them will share the same birthday?

323. Two cars are driving towards each other on the same highway. At this moment, they are 100 kilometers apart. The car driving from the West is travelling at a speed of 40 KPH. The car from the East is travelling at 60 KPH. A bird starts at the same location as the East car and flies above the highway at a speed of 80 KPH. When it reaches the West car, it turns 180 degrees and flies back the way it came, and when it reaches the East car it reverses direction again, and so on ….. How far will the bird have travelled when the two cars meet and pass? In other words, what is the total distance that the bird has travelled when the two cars reach each other?

324. Use maths symbols to replace the question marks in the following equation to make it valid: 12 ? 2 ? 7 ? 4 = 6. (PS can you think of more than one solution?). B) What about 12 ? 2 ? 7 ? 4 = 9?

325. The wall of a small dam (that has a water capacity of about 12,000,000 liters) develops a tiny hole. At first, the hole leaks one drop per hour but you are shocked to realize that the leak is doubling every hour, so after 2 hours it is leaking 2 drops per hour; after 3 hours it is leaking 4 drops; after 4 hours the flow has increased to 8 drops, and so on. One drop is about 0.05 ml (so there are 20,000 drops to a liter). Question A) How long will it take to drain the dam? Question B) How empty will it be 2 hours before that?

326. If seven people meet and each shakes hands, just once, with each other, how many handshakes will there be?

327. You have two hourglasses for measuring time. One measures 10 minutes, the other measures 12 minutes. How can you measure 14 minutes?

328. You bet your friend she cannot stand on one leg for 15 minutes without falling over. If you only have a 7-minute hourglass and an 11-minute hourglass, how can you measure 15 minutes?

329. If it rained for 40 days and 40 nights and the animals went into the ark 2 by 2 at a rate of 30 pairs per day, how many days did it take Moses to load 360 animals?

330. 7 men were travelling slowly along a path when it began to rain; 6 of them tried to quicken their steps but got wet. The 7th stayed as he was and remained quite dry. He did not have an umbrella or hat. How could this be?

331. You go to visit a new supermarket and find that it has an interesting promotion to encourage customers to spend more. They give customers £2 cash back and 1 point for every £10 that they spend. You have £118 cash. How many points can you collect?

332. You have a revolver handgun that has six bullet chambers. You want to shoot a target with as few attempts as possible and you only have two bullets. You get 10 points for shooting the target in one attempt, 7 if it takes 2 attempts, 4 for 3, and 1 if it takes 4 attempts. To make it interesting, someone else puts the 2 bullets side by side (in consecutive chambers) and spins the chambers. You point and pull the trigger but nothing happens. You now have a choice – spin again or not. Should you spin the chamber again or take the next shot without spinning?

333. Chose any number. Decrease it by 50%, then increase what you get by 90%. Is the new number more than, equal to or less than the number you started with?

334. Three friends go to a horserace club together and bet £30 on a horse in one of the races. The horse does not win but it comes third and they win £5 prizemoney. They give 2 £1 coins to a person who is collecting money for a charity. On the way home they try to work out how much they each spent. They each paid £10 towards the bet and got £1 back so they ended up paying just £9 each and gave £2 to charity – or did they? 3 times 9 = 27 plus 2 = 29 not 30. What happened to the other £1?

335. I am a Fibonacci number divisible by 4 and 2. Turn me on my side and I am everything. Cut me in half and I am nothing. What am I?

336. You are a thief robbing a bank. There are 10 sacks of gold coins in the vault and you know that 9 of these are fake; only one of the sacks has real gold in it. Alongside your tools of the trade, you can only fit one of the bags into your backpack. The coins all look the same but a real gold coin weighs exactly 1.01 ounces while fake gold coins weigh just 1.00 ounces. There is a very accurate weighing scale in the room and it is large enough for you to place all the sacks on it at once, but you know that as soon as you use the scale it will set the alarms off and you will need to get out immediately. How can you pick the bag of real gold using the scale only once?

337. What comes next in the sequence: 7, 8, 5, 5, 3, 4, 4, 6, 9, 7, 8?

338. You have just started a new office job and it is your first day at work. You look out of your 3rd-floor window at the part of the car park directly below your window. There are six parking spaces. The numbering system seems strange and at first, you cannot figure it out. The spaces are all empty except for one; there is a car parked in the second space from the right (the 5th space from the left). The other 5 spaces are numbered: 16 06 68 88 – 98. What is the number that is covered by the car?

339. Freddy wants to cover his whole garden in the grass. It is about 10 meters wide by 50 meters long. He is going to use some miracle grass that doubles in size every day. He works out that if he buys 1 square meter of this grass, it will take 10 days to complete the lawn. How much quicker will the lawn be completed if he buys 2 square meters of miracle grass?

340. Your grandfather clock strikes midnight and you ask yourself how many times will the longer hand of this old clock pass the shorter (hour) hand before it starts to strike midnight again?

341. Use any of these symbols (+ or – or x or /) to make sense of the following: I0 I0 I0 = 9:50

342. You are on a management training course with 2 other people. The trainer explains the next test / lesson. She writes a different number on each of your foreheads. She says that 2 of these numbers add up to the other number. She then asks each of you to tell her what your number is. You can see that Leon's number is 2 and Kevin's is 3 but you cannot figure out what that tells you. Leon and Kevin say they do not know how to work this puzzle out either. You consider the situation carefully, weighing up possibilities, and suddenly you figure it out! What is your number?

343. How many degrees are there between clock hands when the time is 03:15?

344. You are a gym teacher. You ask the 15 children in a class to line up and are surprised to see that 7 of them are wearing socks, 5 of them are wearing shoes and 4 are wearing socks and shoes. How many have bare feet?

345. David and Paul are old-school pals who meet from time to time for a game of golf. They have always enjoyed a type of friendly rivalry and like being competitive. David challenges Paul to bet £10 per hole. After playing a few holes, Paul has won 3 bets but David is £50 up; he has won £50 overall. How many holes have they played so far?

346. When you roll 2 dice, what is the most likely score you will get?

347. An old man dies and leaves his precious collection of gold coins and £15,000 to his living relatives. There are 17 identical coins. He leaves half of his fortune to his wife, a third to his son and a sixth to his nephew. How can these three people get their fair share?

348. What is 3/7 chicken, 2/3 cat, and 1/2 goat?

349. You have trouble remembering the code to your bicycle lock so you made up a formula to remind yourself. The code has 5 digits; the fourth number is 4 more than the second number, the second number is 3 more than the third number, the first number is 3 times more than the fifth number, the first two numbers add up to 11 and so do the last two numbers.

350. In the song "The Twelve Days of Christmas", how many gold rings would you have after the 12 days have elapsed?

BRAINTEASERS

351. What are the next 2 letters in this sequence? O,T,T,F,F,S,S.

352. A large, old, wooden sailing yacht with three masts is moored in a harbour. A rope ladder hangs over its side into the water. The rungs of the ladder are 9 inches apart. At the moment, 8 rungs of this ladder are showing above water. The tide rises at 1 foot (12 inches) per hour. It is one hour after low tide. How many rungs will be showing in 4 hours' time?

353. When is L bigger than XL?

354. You wanted to test the law of probability so you have tossed 9 different coins and they have all landed heads up. What is the chance that the 10th coin will be tails?

355. Why does the law say that a man who lives in Glasgow cannot be buried in Paisley?

356. Pauline loves the color purple. Almost everything in her bungalow, except the carpets and the ceilings, is purple – the walls, the kitchen, the toilet, the curtains, the furniture – what color are the stairs?

357. A basket has 6 fresh eggs in it. Six people take one egg each but somehow one egg is left in the basket. How?

358. Can you spell the word candy with just 2 letters?

359. A monkey, a squirrel, and a racoon raced to the top of a coconut tree. Who got to the bananas first?

360. Why did someone drive round and round in so many circles before parking their car?

361. Derek caused havoc when he crept into a restaurant; why did everyone in the restaurant run away, terrified, when they saw him?

362. You have two identical lengths of string fuse but no tape measure. You know that each one will burn from one end to the other in exactly 30 minutes. By burning the fuses, how do you measure 45 minutes' worth of time? You cannot fold or bend or cut them.

363. Before Mount Everest was discovered, what was the highest mountain on Earth?

364. Two old-fashioned objects, that have a similar purpose, come up for sale at an antiques' auction. One has thousands of moving parts the other has no moving parts. What are they?

365. The Earl of Favisham was parked outside a shop. He was fast asleep. A woman suddenly appeared and, without asking or waking him up, quietly got the wheels turning and hurried away. Was he being kidnapped?

366. A young, talented artist has spent many hours working secretly on his new masterpiece. Tired and with the light fading, he decides to go and get some sleep; he will continue and hopefully finish it next week. He is dismayed to find that his work has gone when he returns. No one stole it. What happened?

367. What could you put in a box that would make it lighter? The more of them you put in the box, the lighter it gets – yet it remains empty.

368. Four men sat down to play. They played all night till break of day. They played for money not for fun. With separate scores for everyone. When they came to square accounts, they all had made fair amounts. Can you this paradox explain, if no one lost how could all gain?

369. You have two large jars and 2 empty buckets: one jar is full of yellow marbles the other jar is full of an equal number of red marbles. How can you reorganize things to maximize the chance of someone who is wearing a blindfold selecting a yellow marble from each bucket?

370. Which of these words or phrases is the odd one out? Cat woman, Deus Ex Machina, Parishioner, Pyromania, Scuba.

371. Grandma Brown was concentrating on knitting a complicated sweater when her husband phoned their daughter to tell her their new telephone number. Why did Grandma Brown get angry with him?

372. You are running a management training course for 3 junior managers named Alan, Susan and Julia. You show them 5 stickers, 3 of which have the word YES written on them and 2 have the word NO. You place 3 chairs one behind the other and ask them to sit down. Alan is sitting in the first chair facing forward and cannot see the others. Susan is in the middle chair so she can see Alan's back but not Julia's. Julia is in the last chair so she can see both Susan's and Alan's backs. You place a sticker on each person's back and hide the last 2 stickers. Alan has a YES Susan has a NO and Julia has a YES. You tell them the object of this exercise is to guess which sticker they have on their own back. They are not allowed to talk to each other or turn around. Question a) who will figure it out? (*Stop reading this question while you work this out*). You start a stopwatch and the room falls silent for the next 2 minutes. Question b) Alan gives the correct answer; how did he work it out?

373. What is it that, after you take away the whole, some remains?

374. You hear a story about a woman who died on the operating table while getting a heart transplant. She was officially dead for 5 minutes before the team of doctors was able to revive her. The woman described a strange experience she had while unconscious. She was drawn towards a bright light and came to a beautiful place she guessed was heaven where everyone was naked. Two people came towards her to say hello and she knew they were Adam and Eve before they introduced themselves. How did she work that out?

375. You are the only customer in a bar. The bartender challenges you to a test. If you win, he will give you a free drink – if he wins, you must buy him one. You will put on a blindfold and he will place 4 glasses, in the shape of a square, on a tray, on the bar. Some will be the right way up; some will be upside down - you do not know how many of each there are. He will rotate the tray. Once you are blindfolded, you have to organize the glasses so that they are either all up or all down by giving the barman instructions. The rules are that: in a single turn, any two glasses can be inspected and you can tell the barman to do one of the following three things: 1 reverse the status (upright or upside-down) of either of these glasses, 2 reverse the status (upright or upside-down) of both the glasses, 3 leave the glasses as they are, i.e., no change. After each turn, the square tray is rotated randomly. How can you make sure that all glasses are either up or down? The barman will tell you if you manage to do it. Can you come up with the right set of instructions?

376. In Shakespeare's play "The Merchant of Venice" what lateral thinking solution did the lawyer, Portia, think up to defend her client from losing a pound of flesh?

377. Madame Mystery was a well-known fortune teller and psychic who was famous for predicting events and foretelling the future. She made such a good living at this that a jealous competitor, Old Mr. Briskett, challenged her to a test. Briskett said that Madame Mystery had to guess if the mouse he had in his pocket was alive or dead. Madame Mystery guessed what he was up to, refused the challenge and seemed to back down. Why, what did she guess he was up to?

378. Four boys, Mathew, Mark, Luke and John were having a snowball fight in the street one afternoon after a heavy fall of snow. When a snowball smashed through retired policeman Mr. Robinson's front window, he ran to the front door and shouted at the boys to own up and tell him who did it. They laughed and ran off. He went to visit a neighbor, who had been watching what was going on, but the neighbor refused to make an official statement, scared of what the boys might do to him. All the neighbor was prepared to do was write one symbol on a piece of paper. He drew a? Why was that helpful?

379. Aladdin tells you that he found a magic lamp, rubbed it and a genie appeared. The genie offered him just one wish so he asked for time to think and went home to talk to his wife, mother and father. They were all delighted but their requests were very different. His wife asked that the genie grant them a son, his blind mother asked to regain her sight and his father asked that they be given a big house with a garden. Can you think of one wish that Aladdin could ask the genie which would make as many of his family as possible happy?

380. Tom's car had a puncture so he stopped at the side of the road to change the wheel. He jacked the car up and undid the 4-wheel nuts, but when he put the nuts down on the road, they rolled into a storm drain and were lost. Oh No, he thought, I'm stuck; what do I do now? A woman, who had been watching, came over and made a suggestion which allowed him to drive off. What did she suggest?

381. An old man has just sold his precious, 10-foot long, antique, 2-piece, split-cane trout fishing rod on eBay. It is kept in its original 5-foot-long bag. When he gets to the post office, he is told that they do not accept parcels longer than 4 foot. Can you think of a way that he can get around this restriction and post the fishing rod at the post office?

382. You are one of the organizers of an annual Mountain Race. 80 runners have registered and arrived to take part in this challenging test. The route takes them 10 miles of rough terrain, through a steep ravine, over a high ridge and down a rocky path. Runners have occasionally been injured or become lost going the wrong way in the past. The person who was supposed to be in charge of making sure that everyone gets back to the finish has just called off sick. You will have to take over this role. The only technology you brought with you is a calculator. The runners wear numbers from 1 to 80. Is there a way you could use the calculator to work out if they all reach the finish line? Your solution should also tell you which runner is missing if someone does lose their way.

383. What do the following have in common: AKL, AGP, CMN, CPT, DFW, KIX, MUC, RAK, SCL, SFO, YYZ, and ZRH?

384. Ann was on holiday in Rockingham and after visiting an art shop, she went into a local café, sat down at a table near the front window and ordered a large Americano coffee. The waitress brought it over to her. Ann had only just started to sip her coffee when a big housefly fell into it. She called the waitress back and asked for a fresh cup of coffee. The waitress took the cup away, but when she brought the new coffee Ann said it was not fresh; she said the waitress had just removed the fly and brought the same coffee back. How did she know?

---

385. What letter comes next in the following sequence? D R M F S L T _?

---

386. You are the referee of a golf championship, appointed by the committee to oversee the rules and ensure everyone in the competition plays fairly. Someone approaches you and says they suspect that one of the players is going to cheat by using a slightly heavier (non-regulation) golf ball. You ask the 12 players to show you the balls they will play with – they all look identical. You have a balance scale you could weigh them on but you can only use it three times. Can you figure out which ball, if any, is overweight?

---

387. In Round 1 of a knockout competition, the Snipsnaps beat the Book-sellers, the Newspaper-editors beat the Pebbles, the Cobbles beat the Cutters and the Speech-writers were beaten by the Shearers. In round 2 the Snipsnaps beat the Newspaper-editors and the Cobbles beat the Shearers. The Cobbles won the final. What is this competition?

388. You are playing table tennis in a large shed with a concrete floor when the only ping pong ball you have rolls into a corner and drops down a 1-foot (30 cm) deep cylindrical hole in the concrete. The hole is not much wider than the ball. Is there a way to get the ball out undamaged? (There is more than one answer).

389. Two trains are crossing the USA from coast to coast, a journey of about 3,000 miles. One is travelling from the west towards the east at 90 MPH. The other is travelling from east to west at 70MPH. Which train will be closer to the Pacific coast when they meet?

390. A famous Formula 1 racing driver anticipated that there had been a bad crash in a Grand Prix before he could see it. He slammed the brakes on halfway around a long bend in the track and skidded to a halt just before hitting the pile-up of race cars strewn across the track. How did he guess there had been a pile-up? There were no warning lights or flags, he could not see around the bend and there was no sign of smoke or flames. How did he judge that something was wrong?

391. 3 teachers are supervising 3 disobedient children. The children were reported missing and the teachers were sent to bring them back. The teachers searched the woods a few miles away, found the children and set out to walk them back to school. The group takes a shortcut and needs to cross a river. There is a little boat that can only take 3 people at a time. Children cannot be left alone or they might run off again; a teacher must supervise them. How can the teachers get all the children across the river?

---

392. Your two children are fighting over a tub of ice cream. They say that you will give one of them more than the other. Without weighing the bowls, can you think of a way to solve this argument?

---

393. A car, a shout of approval, a name, a wing, a sound, a dance, a sport, a place to stay, a country, a girl's name, a weight, a city, another name, a month, an award, a grandfather, a province, half a play, open country, another dance, clothing, a winner, a drink, a medical device, a baseball team and an African tribe. What are the names of the girl, the country, the province, the play, the award and the baseball team?

---

394. You go on holiday with 4 friends and visit a historic site thousands of years old. At one moment, while the 5 of you are exploring the site, you realize that you are standing in such a way that you are all at an equal distance away from each other. In other words, the distance between any two friends is the same. How can this be?

---

395. A farmer decides to give his son a test. He gives him some money and tells him to go to town and buy **one** thing that will provide them with something to eat and drink, something to plant and something to give the pig.

396. It is the middle of a pandemic lockdown. No one is allowed to travel far and you live over a hundred miles from your daughter. She is talking about getting married and you would like to give your daughter her great grandmother's precious jewellery box which contains an ancient wedding ring, a string of pearls and some antique brooches. You could post it to her; the trouble is, if you do that, you worry that someone might open the box and take whatever they want. The jewellery box can be locked with a padlock and you come up with a plan. What can you do to ensure that no one, except your daughter, can open the box?

397. A new virulent virus is highly infectious. Every day the total number of people infected with it doubles. If it takes 60 days to infect everyone in Europe, how many days does it take to infect an eighth of Europe?

398. There were four people at a family get-together: a mother, father, a son, a daughter, an aunt, an uncle, a brother, a sister, a cousin, a nephew and a niece. Is this possible?

399. Which letter comes next in the series: A B G D E Z E _?

400. On hearing that an inspector is coming to a school to assess the knowledge of the students and the quality of the teaching, one of the teachers tells the students in her class what to do when the inspector visits. The inspector is astonished when, having given the teacher a list of questions to ask the class, almost all of the students put their hands up in response to every question. Not only that, but the students that the teacher selects to answer each question always give a good answer. What did the teacher tell the students to do?

AMUSING

401. Why is it that when you look for something, it is always in the last place you thought of?

402. You are looking down from a first-floor balcony at the concrete path 5 meters below. How can you drop a raw egg without cracking it?

403. What time is it when an elephant sits on a fence?

404. You look out of the window one morning and see a hat, a carrot, 3 black stones and a scarf lying on the lawn. Why are these objects on the lawn?

405. A man is trapped in a room with no windows or doors. The only items in the room are a table and a mirror. How does he escape?

406. What is an important difference between a jeweler and a jailer?

407. What can go up a chimney down but can't go down a chimney up?

408. Harry is 6 foot tall; he works in a butcher's shop; he has a 35-inch waist circumference and he has a size 10 shoe size; what does he weigh?

409. What has four wheels and flies?

410. What do Winnie the Pooh and Alexander the Great have in common?

411. Which land animal cannot go backwards?

412. According to the Hitch Hiker's Guide to the Galaxy, what is the answer to the ultimate question of life, the universe, and everything?

413. What has a bottom at the top?

414. Who were Thomas Crapper and Otto Titslinger, and what are they famous for?

415. What type of cheese is made backwards?

416. When Dawn and Bert moved into a new house, Bert was unhappy to discover that the previous occupants had left a big, friendly cat behind. This cat seemed to think it owned the place. Why was Bert so unhappy?

417. What can you make that is invisible?

418. A bus driver and a doctor are both in love with the same woman. The bus driver knew that he had to go on a bus trip that would last a week, so before he left, he gave the woman seven apples. Why?

419. What kind of vegetable needs a plumber?

420. What is it illegal to do in French vineyards?

421. What is often made of leather and sounds like a sneeze?

422. A man goes into a house; no one is home; he enters a room, gets a fright, raises his arms, turns around and laughs. Why?

423. What do Americans do over 20 times a day, on average?

424. Who is bigger: Mr. Bigger, Mrs. Bigger, or their baby?

425. In the early days of the Space Program, scientists needed to develop a pen that could write in the weightless environment of space. Normal pens of the day relied on atmospheric pressure or gravity (both of which were inadequate in outer space) to operate. Millions of dollars were spent developing a pressurized pen to solve this difficult problem. What was the simple solution?

426. A man wanted to prove his love to his wife, so he climbed the highest mountain, swam the deepest ocean and crossed the widest desert. How did his wife show her gratitude?

427. What did Iceland divert roads to avoid?

428. Your friend tells you that she can predict the score of any football or rugby game before the game starts! How can she do that? She is not psychic.

429. How can you make the number one disappear?

430. A sign outside a farm shop says: "*Some days we open at 9, some days it's 12, some days we don't open at all; lately we've been here a lot unless we are not here. Please note, if you want to buy chickens, ducks or geese, you can get 2 chickens for a duck, 2 chickens and a duck for 2 geese. Buy 3 geese, one chicken and 2 ducks for £25 exactly, no change given!*" Can you work out the price of a duck?

DETECTIVE STORIES

431. The police phone a man to tell him that his wife has been murdered. Shocked and horrified, the man jumps into his car and drives to the scene of the crime to identify the body. Why do the police arrest him?

432. Brian is accused of murdering his wife. Her body has not been found and he says she ran away one day and has never been seen since. Brian's lawyer defends Brian by saying that there is no proof she is dead. The lawyer says that he has tracked the wife down and has asked her to appear in court today to prove she is still alive. The lawyer says she will come through the door at the back of the courtroom when called and he invites everyone to watch her enter. Everyone in the courtroom turns around and stares at the door in anticipation but when the lawyer calls out the wife's name, no one appears. Then the lawyer says with a flourish, "*You see, that proves you are not convinced that my client murdered his wife, otherwise you would not have turned around and looked.*" The judge, who watched this performance carefully, announces that he thinks Brian is guilty. How did he reach that conclusion?

433. Very late one night, a man wearing black clothes, a balaclava and gloves enters a house by the unlocked back door and climbs the stairs. He goes straight to one of the bedrooms takes out a gun and shoots an old man, who is in bed, three times, and kills him. The old man makes no attempt to hide or call out; it is as if he expected this to happen. The killer knocks a few things off tables and shelves and smashes the back door window before leaving but does not steal anything. Can you make sense of this event?

---

434. A neighbor reported hearing a sound like a gunshot in the house next door. No one answered the doorbell when the police arrived to investigate. They went inside and discovered an apparent suicide. A dead man was slumped on a couch with a revolver in his hand. There was a tape recorder beside him and when the police pressed the Play button, they heard the following: "I hate my life, I can't go on" followed by the sound of a gunshot. Based on this evidence, how did the police know he had been murdered?

---

435. A man wearing a backpack is found in the middle of a muddy field; he is almost dead. With his last breaths, he says that he knew he was going to die but could do nothing to avoid it. There are no footprints near him or objects of importance in the field. He was not killed by a person or animal, and he did not kill himself. He had been perfectly healthy. He did not die of old age, a heart attack, or other health conditions. He was not poisoned. He had no allergies. He was not killed by an act of God (e.g., lightning, hail). How did he die?

---

436. A married couple, well known for fighting and arguing with each other, have a huge row one evening and the wife storms off to her room furious, locks her bedroom door, lights the gas fire to warm the room and gets into bed to read a book and calm down. Her sister comes to visit her the next day. She finds the bedroom door locked and gets no answer when she knocks. She can smell gas, so she calls the fire brigade who break the door down. The wife is dead in bed, asphyxiated. The room stinks of gas but the gas fire is off. Suspicion falls on the husband but it is accepted that he could not have entered the room. Despite this, her sister thinks he is guilty – how does she think he did it?

437. There has been a murder at a school. It is 9 am on the day before the first day of the new term, after the Christmas holidays, and the headmaster has been found dead at his desk. The attending detective asked to speak to everyone who had been in the school at the time of the recent murder. The History teacher said he was in the library doing research; the English teacher said he was reading the newspaper in the teachers' common room, the Mathematics teacher said he was marking exam papers, the PT teacher said he was checking the gym equipment and the Science teacher said he was setting up experiments in the lab. Who did the detective suspect was not telling the truth?

438. A woman killed her husband and tried to fool the police in a clever way. She shot him while he slept in bed, made a mess of the house, injured herself and blamed a masked burglar. To confuse the detectives and appear innocent, she put misleading prints on the murder weapon. How did she do that?

439. The guards of an open prison have all been given strict instructions not to allow any prisoner to leave without authorized release papers and not to allow any visitors to enter without written permission from the governor. Guards who watch the long path, which is the only way in and out, know that it takes at least 5 minutes for anyone to travel from one end to the other, so they check the path every 4 minutes. One of the reasons it takes so long to walk the length of the path is that it has 5 gates that must be opened and closed quietly. Given these facts, how did a prisoner make a successful escape without release papers?

440. Two detectives are sent to investigate a man's death. His body lies face down on the ground next to an empty, abandoned apartment block that is due for demolition. The apartment block is 20 stories high and every apartment has a balcony. They have a quick look around and one detective decides this must be another suicide; there had been three others in this area in the last month. The other detective is not so sure – he wants to check which balcony the man may have jumped off so he goes into the building and carefully works his way up the levels. He goes into all the apartments that face the direction of the body, looking for evidence, unlocking the glass doors to the balconies and checking the floor and railings of every balcony on every floor. When he returns, he tells the other detective he is sure this was a murder. How did he work that out?

441. Following a tip-off, a team of FBI agents burst into an apartment to arrest a suspected murderer. All they know is that his name is Alfred. They find a plumber, a truck driver, a bricklayer and a bank manager playing poker in a smoky room. They have no hesitation in arresting the truck driver; why?

---

442. A policeman was interviewing the wife of a man who had died suddenly. She explained that her husband had complained that the scary, gory horror film he had watched earlier in the evening had affected his dreams. He told her that in his dream, he was chased by a huge monster through a forest to the edge of a cliff and found himself looking down over a 1,000-foot drop. Trapped and terrified, he could hear the beast rampaging towards him. Just then, his wife woke him. The shock was so great the poor man died immediately on the spot. Why did the policemen arrest the wife?

---

443. A powerful and fearsome dictator invited his enemies to a fabulous, no-expense-spared party. The only liquid refreshment available was a special, iced punch drink in a huge bowl. At the start of the evening, everyone was given a glass of this delicious fruity juice as a toast and they returned many times to refill their glasses. One visitor had to leave early. The next day all the guests died except for the early departing visitor. He did have a drink of the punch before he left. Why did he survive?

---

444. A man heard a knock on his front door. He opened it to find a policeman in uniform who asked him, “*Are you Mr. William Woods married to Mary Woods*”. The man replied “*yes*”. The policeman said, “*I am sorry to tell you that your brother-in-law has been murdered*”. William replied, “*Oh my goodness, poor Michael, my wife will be devastated; I better tell her.*” When Mary comes to the door, the policeman asks her if she knows anyone that might have wanted to kill Michael and she admits that there has been a lot of arguments among her three brothers about their inheritance. As soon as she said this, the policemen arrested William; why?

445. The police were called when a man was found hanging from a tree in the middle of a forest north of Thunder Bay. He was dead. It looked like he had been there for some time. The police determined that this had been an accident, not a suicide, and called the fire brigade and an undertaker. How did they know it was not a suicide?

446. A teenager took his new birthday present out to the park to play with it. An hour later the police arrested him, confiscated the present, accused him of murder with a dangerous weapon and threw him in jail. The boy's lawyer argued that it was an unfortunate accident and no dangerous weapon was involved. Any idea what happened?

447. Robert Wilson explained to his cellmate, Jack Stone, that he had been jailed for manslaughter; he said that the prosecuting lawyer had not been able to prove he had murdered his victim deliberately. Robert admitted that he had been lucky because he did actually carry out his plan to kill the victim in cold blood. Jack Stone confided in Robert that he, too had been lucky; he told Robert that he had been a contract killer but had only been jailed for a violent fight he had been involved in. He mentioned several unsolved murder cases and described how he had committed these crimes without being caught. A few days later, Robert was transferred and his appeal for release was accepted. How can this leniency be explained?

448. A rich widow who owned a large country house estate came home one day and, when she looked through the dining room bay windows, was terrified to see a man hit a woman several times. She was too frightened to intervene and did not even call for help from her live-in butler. Can you think why she acted this way?'

449. Sherlock Holmes was asked to explain how a man had died, it looked like the man had committed suicide but no one could work out how he had managed it. The man was found hanging in the middle of a big room behind a supermarket distribution warehouse near Las Vegas in mid-summer. The rope was tied to the rafters and his feet were about 3 feet above the floor. Apart from the hanged man, the room was empty. The question was what did he stand on or jump off?

450. Why did a travel agent phone the police to report a murder when he read that a politician's wife had died, rather mysteriously, while on holiday?

REAL WORLD

---

451. Why do so many moose hunters in the wilds of Canada get shot?

---

452. What do the game of cricket and an acre have in common?

---

453. The introduction of a new UK Passport Agency IT system led to long delays (which cost an estimated £12m). Four years later, the system was working well with 99.5% of straightforward applications being turned around within 10 days. What did the passport agency do in 1999 to try to apologize to people waiting in long queues outside passport offices?

---

454. A change in the law in Italy resulted in a sudden run of sales of white T shirts with a black diagonal stripe – why?

---

455. Described as elegant, slender and graceful at the time, the first Tacoma Narrows bridge was the third longest suspension span in the world when it was built in 1940, but it collapsed just four months after it was opened. What caused this dramatic and serious failure?

---

456. A man from Japan had a specific and clear ambition, he wanted to attain a certain goal or achievement in the sport he loved and although he was keen to make it happen, he took out insurance in case it did. What was his ambition/goal and why did he take out insurance?

---

457. Why are manholes round instead of square?

---

458. Spinach consumption rose by 33% in the USA in 1931. What is the main reason given for this?

---

459. What is so special about the world record set by Johann Hurlinger in 1900? Hint: it has something to do with a journey he made from Vienna to Paris.

---

460. What should you do after eating a meal when in the Gilbertese Islands?

461. When it was built in 1929, the Empire State Building achieved its objectives. It was completed well ahead of schedule, well below budget and reached its main project objective - which was that it must be the highest building in New York (beating the Chrysler Building). These days it is 97% occupied and world-famous, but it was a financial flop for decades. Why was it a success as a building project but a failure as a commercial project initially?

462. What was the main point of the 1961 Milgram experiment, in which volunteer participants were led to believe they were assisting in an education research program to test positive and negative reinforcement tactics on learning? The participants were told they must ask a person in another room questions and give them a nasty electronic shock every time that person gave a wrong answer, then turn the voltage up a notch and administer a higher dose next time and so on. What was this experiment actually measuring?

463. Why did the Greeks leave the Trojans a present of a large wooden horse when they gave up their fruitless 10-year siege of Troy?

464. Greenland is a huge country covered in snow and ice. Why did the man who discovered it call it Greenland?

465. In 2004, Airbus was hoping to launch the biggest passenger plane in the skies. It was a huge, expensive, pan-European, collaboration project. Parts were shipped from Toulouse to Hamburg for assemblage but a serious problem soon became apparent. What went wrong?

466. In World War 2, why did soldiers shoot dogs that they had so carefully trained?

467. Although there is relatively few left-handed golf tour professionals, most golf clubs prefer to employ left-handed golf professionals as coaches. Why?

468. In medieval battles, archers often raised their hand and gave the enemy a two finger "salute" - making a V shape with their fingers - in a defiant way that would be regarded as a very rude gesture these days. What did this sign signify – what was their message?

469. What clever defense did a lawyer in Scotland propose, in court, to the jury, to defend someone who had been caught climbing out of a fur shop skylight with 6 expensive fur coats late at night by two policemen?

470. Why did the (then) expensive and complicated new technique of taking arial photographs, which enhanced accurate map making, help to increase the income of the UK government?

471. After years of painstaking research, what did Ignaz Semmelweis (1818 to 1865) eventually discover was the reason why so many more women died of so called "childbed fever" in one maternity hospital compared to another similar hospital?

472. The world's first postage stamp, the famous Penny Black, was introduced in Britain in 1840. The idea was a great success and was later taken up worldwide. Yet the Penny Black was only in use for one year before it was replaced by the Penny Red. Why?

473. What was "The Ghost Army", why was it kept secret for 50 years and why is it a good example of lateral thinking?

474. A female member of a film crew was shot while working on location by an actor. She died. How did this happen?

475. A healthy, 60-year-old man went into hospital and insisted that they remove one of his kidneys. No one he knew had kidney disease and he did not sell it. Why did he do it?

476. Why did someone record the painting he did on a boiled egg in an egg register?

477. Patients at a children's hospital adored the cuddly animal toys that the hospital provided; the children loved to play with the teddy bears and other soft toy creatures. In fact, they liked them so much that these toys were disappearing at an alarming rate. How did the hospital stop the children from taking so many toys home?

478. Canada passed a strict gun-control law in 1995, which required universal regulation of guns, including rifles and shotguns. Proponents said the central registry would give law-enforcement agencies a powerful new tool for tracking weapons used in crimes and it would help to reduce domestic violence and suicide. The budget for a new gun registration database was $2 million (Canadian) and it was estimated that this would soon be paid off by the registration fee that gun owners would pay. What went wrong?

479. You may have heard that there is a way to get a ship into a bottle but how would you get a full-sized pear into a bottle without damaging the pear or the bottle?

480. Why was the judgment of Solomon so successful?

481. Cowboys who were around in the days of the wild west lived dangerous lives. They were threatened by disease, gunfights, stampedes, rattlesnakes, and bad or not enough food, but these are not what killed most of them. What was the most common cause of death among cowboys in the 1800s?

482. Zoologists and ornithologists agree that there is a good reason why birds' eggs are such a distinctive shape – narrower at one end than the other – what is the reason?

483. German chemist August Kekulé had spent many years studying carbon-carbon bonds but was stuck in his research of the annular structure of benzene. He could not figure it out until one day when he thought laterally and visualized a long row of atoms forming an ouroboros. What did he visualize that gave him the answer he was searching for?

484. When the famous dancer Isadora Duncan was found strangled, why did the police not suspect murder?

485. King George IV (who was King from 1820 to 1830) is credited with what trend in footwear? In what significant way were his shoes different from most peoples'?

486. Why did Scottish scientist Alexander Fleming not throw away his experiment when he noticed mould growing on it? What conclusion did he reach that led to a very important discovery?

487. Over 400 people died in a terrible fire in a nightclub called 'The Coconut Grove' in 1942. Why were all public building regulations changed because of this tragic event? What was the mistake in the building's design and manufacture that led to the death toll being so high?

488. In the 1960s, Spencer Silver, a chemist at 3M, was trying to developing a super-strong adhesive. Instead, he accidentally created a weak adhesive that could be unstuck easily without leaving a residue. A few years later, his colleague, Art Fry, realized the potential this adhesive had for creating an innovative product. What product?

489. Why do men's shirts have buttons on the right while women's buttons are on the left?

490. A man in his mid-40s, wearing a business suit with a black tie and white shirt, who called himself Dan Cooper, bought a one-way airline ticket on Flight #305, bound for Seattle, Washington on November 24, 1971. He ordered a bourbon and soda while the flight was waiting to take off and handed the stewardess a note saying that he had a bomb in his briefcase. He demanded four parachutes and $200,000 in twenty-dollar bills. These items were brought on board. The plane took off heading for Mexico City and sometime later, the hijacker told the pilot to descend to 10,000 feet and parachuted to freedom with all the money. He was never found. Why did he ask for four parachutes?

491. Why did American funk band Vulfpeck create an album called Sleepify that contained no music, make it available on the music streaming service Spotify and encourage consumers to play the album on a loop while they slept? The album had no audible sound; it just consisted of ten roughly 30-second-long tracks of silence.

492. Many allied fighter and bomber planes were shot down during World War 2. Planes returned from missions riddled with bullet holes. One day someone suggested that these planes should be studied to see where the typical pattern of holes were so that these parts could be given armor plating. This idea was turned down and a very different strategy was adopted. Why, and what was the new strategy?

---

493. How do the publishers of atlases and dictionaries often protect their work from copyright infringers?

---

494. In Taiwan, a rich man's son was kidnapped. The ransom note demanded that the father bring 10 valuable diamonds to a phone box in the middle of a park. Further instructions would be left in the phone box and no one but the father was to go anywhere near it. Plain clothes police surrounded the park. The rich man went to the phone box alone, with the diamonds, and followed instructions. The police were powerless to stop the kidnapper getting the diamonds and he was not caught. What did the inventive kidnapper do?

---

495. George Washington was born on February the 11ᵗʰ 1732, but after 1752 his birthday became February 22ⁿᵈ. Why?

---

496. Millions of people died of smallpox in the 18ᵗʰ century. An English County doctor named Edward Jenner (1749 o 1823) is credited as the person who figured out a way to defeat this scourge. He noticed that dairymaids did not get the disease and developed a treatment to prevent it. Why did dairymaids not get smallpox and what did he base his treatment on?

497. The "Global Biomass of Wild Mammals" report estimated the proportions of the earth's biomass of humans, domesticated mammals and wild (marine and terrestrial) mammals. What percentage of the world's mammal biomass is attributed to wild land mammals?

498. How was Aeschylus, the ancient Greek playwright, killed by a tortoise?

499. When Archduke Ferdinand was shot in 1914, his attendants could not undo his coat quickly enough to stem the bleeding in time to save him. Why not? (PS it has been suggested that this issue was responsible, in part at least, for the outbreak of the First World War.)

500. The movie "Jaws" hit a big problem while filming in 1974. The script focused on a terrifying monster shark which appeared in many scenes. The trouble was that the mechanical shark they were using developed too many mechanical and technical faults and was not convincing. Delays and holdups meant the movie was over budget and over schedule. Director Steven Spielberg did some lateral thinking to escape these problems and created one of the best films of the time. What was his clever solution?

501. A man who wanted someone to build an extension to his house approached several builders, showed them his drawings and plans and asked if they were interested in quoting for the work. One of the builders offered to do the job for free – why?

502. According to legend, a portrait of James, Duke of Monmouth, painted in 1695, was very unusual. Why?

503. What was the main reason why the financial services company "The State Street Corporation" commissioned a statue of a "confident" young girl with hands on hips and placed it in front of (facing/staring down) the famous Wall Street charging bull statue? Named the Fearless Girl, it appeared to promote the importance of women working in corporate leadership roles but was that the real reason they did it – according to many people?

504. Why were more WW1 soldiers injured if they wore metal helmets that if they wore cloth caps?

505. What remarkable world record did James Hargris and Charles Creighton achieve in their Ford Model A car in 42 days in 1930?

506. A 250-year-old cemetery in the middle of a European city was running out of room to bury any more bodies. The management committee did not want to disinter or dig up any old graves but they wanted to be able to provide resting places for as many people as possible in the future. Someone suggested a radical solution – what was it?

507. Horses have 4 "natural" gaits, which are, in increasing order of speed, the walk, trot, canter, and gallop. The walk is a 4-beat gait. What are the trot, canter and gallop? Are they 2, 3 or 4 beat gaits?

508. The Sydney Opera House is a world-famous, iconic building which hosts around 1500 performances and has millions of visitors each year, but by many measures it was a project failure. How much over budget and over schedule was it when it was built?

509. The 1971 Stanford prison experiment, led by psychology professor Philip Zimbardo, was supposed to last 2 weeks. Male students were recruited via a newspaper advert which offered $15 a day to those who wanted to participate in a "psychological study of prison life." Volunteers were chosen after assessments of psychological stability and then randomly assigned to be prisoners or prison guards. Those volunteers selected to be "guards" were given a pair of dark sunglasses and a peaked hat to see if that helped them to adopt a more authoritarian attitude.

They were instructed to prevent prisoners from escaping. What happened and how long did the experiment run for?

---

510. Why was a man who was thrown in a Caribbean jail in the middle of 1902 and neglected - (abandoned without water and food for days) – grateful for the experience for the rest of his life (another 27 years)? The solitary-confinement jail cell was bomb-proof, did not have any windows and was ventilated only through a narrow grating under the door.

ELIMINATION

511. Anne, Jeremy, Marie and Bob went to an activity center for a holiday. They tried: orienteering, canoeing, rock climbing, and trampolining. Each person found that they had a different favorite activity. Anne's favorite is not rock climbing. Jeremy is very scared of heights but not scared of water. Marie needs a harness to do her favorite activity. Bob always wants to keep his feet on the ground. Who likes what?

512. A woman is asked what her daughters look like. She answers: *"They are all blonds but two, all brunettes but two and all redheads but two"*. How many daughters does she have?

513. Five people - Alison, Bruce, Charlie, Fred, and Sarah – meet at an allergy treatment clinic. They are each allergic to something different: pollen, shellfish, bee stings, cats, or nuts. Alison has a food allergy. Bruce lives with a cat and a dog at his home. Charlie's allergy is not related to animals. Fred has seasonal allergies. Who is allergic to what?

514. You have read a report that says that the 80 politicians in a certain political party are either liars or truth tellers, one or the other. The report goes on to say that at least one of them is honest (a truth teller) and that if you take any two politicians, at least one will be a liar. Knowing this, how many of the 80 are probably liars and how many are honest?

---

515. Five students have gone on holiday to Athens together. It is their first time abroad and they are excited to discover so many new things. They go to a fancy night club and start talking to the barman. On the shelves behind the bar, there are all sorts of bottles with strange shapes and names. Enjoying their company, the barman comes up with a challenge. He will give them 3 rounds of drinks free if they can tell him what the names of nine different drinks are once, they have tried them. He assures the students that the drinks will all be very different in taste and color and tells them to sit at a table and he will bring the drinks over. He names the 9 drinks he will provide as Cointreau, Ouzo, Parfait d'amour, Crème de Menthe, Calvados, Port, Advocaat, Sloe Gin and Kahula. They can order them in any order they like. What plan can they come up with to get all the drinks for free?

---

516. You have paid to go on a murder mystery weekend at a hotel. You are the only guest. You arrive on Friday and on Saturday morning, the receptionist tells you that the barman reported finding an old man dead on the floor of an upstairs room last night. He had called for help when he tripped over the body in the dark. The old man had been stabbed. You ask if anyone knew of a reason why the poor old man was killed. *"Did anyone hate him?"* The receptionist said no – not as far as she knew. She continued *"I mean, he was a very grumpy old guest and he had been rude to everyone but was that enough to kill him?"* *"Who else was in the hotel?"* you ask. *"Well, there was the owner, but I think he went to bed very early, the waitress but she said she was watching TV, the gardener said he was going home after dinner and I was reading a book. I don't think* *anyone else was in the hotel at the time." "Tell me more about the barman discovering the body." "Well, I hear he was on the way to bed after a long evening's work when he noticed the body slumped on the floor. I have no idea who could have done it."* Can you figure it out ... who dunnit?

---

517. Four girls went to a dance. Mary wore a yellow dress. Anne did not have a ring. The girl who wore a necklace also wore a red dress. Jennifer wore a bracelet. The girl who wore a blue dress also wore earrings. Lucy did not wear earrings or a black dress. Who wore what?

---

518. You are given an ordinary deck of 52 playing cards and told that 13 of them are face up and the rest are face down. The face up cards are distributed randomly throughout the deck. You are blindfolded and asked to create 2 piles of cards with the same number of cards face up. How can you do that?

---

519. Mother, father, brother and sister were all at home when it happened. Facts – a) One of the four killed one of the others. b) One of them saw who did the murder. c) The other person helped with the killing. d) The father is the oldest member of the family. e) The person who did the killing is not the youngest. f) The youngest person and the person who was killed are not the same sex. g) The person who helped the killer was older than the person who was killed. h) The person who witnessed the murder and the person who helped are not of the same sex. i) The oldest person and the witness are the same sex. Questions: Who did the killing and who was killed?

520. Tim, Jeff and Caroline are spies, either secret agents or traitors. Tim is a CIA agent. Caroline is a traitor. Tim is spying on Jeff and Jeff is spying on Caroline. Can you tell if a secret agent is spying on a traitor – yes or no?

521. You are an amateur archaeologist on the holiday of a lifetime, exploring caves miles from civilization. Your research tells you these caves may have been inhabited thousands of years ago and are unlikely to have been visited for decades. You set out from your campsite early one morning and enter a complex cave system. You are thrilled to see signs of ancient human life including primitive paintings. You venture on. Suddenly the ceiling of the cave behind you collapses, blocking your return, and you realize with a growing sense of unease that you are lost. You have been in the caves for about 3 hours; your phone does not work here, no one knows how to find you. You come to a junction and, to your surprise, find 5 exit doors. Clearly, you are not the only person to have visited recently. Having studied the local language, you can make sense of what is written on each door. They all seem to offer ways out but have ominous warnings: the first says beware of the swarm of deadly hornets, the second warns of an infestation of cobras and rattle snakes, the third says you will have to swim through a pool of bloodthirsty piranhas, the fourth warns it is crammed with vampire bats and the fifth mentions thousands of poisonous spiders and tarantulas. Which route will you choose (if any)?

522. Micky, Kenny, John, Arthur, Eric and Samantha meet up for a party. Three of them are teenagers; the other three are their fathers. Samantha went to the recent school dance with Micky's son. Eric and John still play for the school's rugby team and one of them is Arthur's son. Micky and Eric are not related. Can you work out who is who? Which teenagers are related to which fathers?

523. You have to make a momentous decision. It will affect the rest of your life. You need advice. You are told that there are two wise old philosophers who live in different communities in the mountains. The trouble is that one community always tells the truth and the other always lies and says the opposite of what they know and think. You come to a crossroads and meet a person from one of the philosopher groups – but you do not know which one. What question can you ask to be sure of finding the truth-telling community?

524. Elizabeth, Alison and Stanley are friends. One is a nurse, one is a police officer and one is a teacher. Elizabeth is afraid of blood and neither she nor Stanley like children. What is Stanley's job?

525. You are appearing in a popular TV game show. The presenter explains the next challenge. Attached to the wall in front of you are three cabinets. One of the three has £5,000 in it; the other two are empty. A different message is written on each door. The first says "This cabinet does not have the money", the second says "This cabinet has the money", the third says "The second cabinet does not have the money". You are told that only one of these statements is truc; the other two are false. The clock is ticking, the TV audience is watching, you feel the pressure mounting, can you work out which cabinet has the money?

526. There are 6 people on the train. The driver, the conductor, the ticket collector and three passengers named Mr Smith, Mr Jones and Mr. Brown. Remarkably the train staff have the same last names as the passengers; for convenience, we can refer to them without using the prefix "Mr.". This is all we know: 1 Mr. Brown lives in Brixton. 2 the conductor lives in Chelsea, 3 Mr. Jones cannot do algebra, 4 Smith often beats the ticket inspector at snooker, 5 the passenger who shares the conductor's name lives in Tottenham, and 6 the conductor goes to the same local pub as the passenger who is a mathematics teacher. What is the name of the driver?

527. You wake up early one morning, it is still dark and you do not want to wake your partner by switching on the bedroom light. You know you have 53 socks in your drawer: 21 blue, 15 black and 17 red. How many socks do you need to take out to be certain you have at least one pair of black socks?

528. You are going on a 3-week holiday to visit Singapore and you want to employ someone you can trust to look after your house and pets while you are away. You interview 4 candidates Judy, Peter, Sarah and Henry. You know that two are honest and the other two are compulsive liars. They all know each other. Can you work out which two are the liars from what they tell you? Judy says *"Neither Peter nor Henry tell the truth."* Henry says, *"If Sarah is a liar, then Judy is trustworthy."* Peter says, *"If, and only if, Judy is not an honest person, then Sarah also does not care about the truth."* Sarah says, *"What Peter said is untrue."*

529. Joe and Bennie are friends with Christine and they wanted to know when her birthday is. Christine gave them a list of 10 possible dates: May 15, May 16, May 19, June 17, June 18, July 14, July 16, August 14, August 15, and August 17. Christine told Joe and Bennie separately the month and the day of her birthday respectively. Joe said: *I don't know when Cheryl's birthday is, but I know that Bennie does not know too.* Bennie said: *At first, I did not know when Christine's birthday is but I know now.* Joe said: *In that case, I also know when Christine's birthday is.* So when is Christine's birthday?

---

530. There are 4 people in 4 different hotel rooms. Each room has a laptop and webcams. Each person is wearing a Tee shirt which has a large colorful circle printed on the back but they do not know what color their Tee shirt is; they cannot take it off and there are no mirrors in the rooms. There are 2 Tee shirts with Green circles and 2 Tee shirts with Orange circles. Each person has a different view.

a. Person 1 is wearing a Tee shirt with a green circle on the back and can see person 2 and person 3,

b. Person 2 is wearing a Tee shirt with an orange circle and can only see person 3,

c. Person 3 is wearing a Tee shirt with a green circle and cannot see anyone else (their screen is switched off),

d. Person 4 is wearing a Tee shirt with an orange circle and cannot see anyone else. The other 3 people cannot see them. (Their camera and screen are switched off).

Which person will be the first to guess what color Tee shirt they are wearing and why?

MYSTERIES

531. Can you think of any reasons to explain why the hair on a man's head tends to go grey long before the hair in his mustache?

---

532. It has been suggested that this scenario is used the test candidates who want to join the CIA. There are (at least) 2 versions. Candidates are asked to give an explanation that makes sense of these scenarios.

- Version A) Three men gather in the corner of a golf club bar one afternoon. They all have something in common but they are not there to play golf. They sit in silence most of the time and appear to be waiting. A delivery van arrives and a sealed cool box, which has their names on the address label, is handed over. The parcel inside the box is well wrapped in plastic and newspaper and ice. They unwrap the parcel and find it contains a human arm. They nod to each other and go their separate ways. One of them takes the cool box and dumps it in a garbage skip.

- Version B) A well-dressed surgeon ventures into the seedier part of town looking for a homeless, down-and-out man about the same size and age as he is and offers them $25,000 for their left arm. The deal he proposes is that he will give them the money if they allow him to surgically remove their arm.

How do these accounts make sense? Why were the 3 men in the golf club content to see the arm and why did the surgeon want to purchase a left arm?

533. Eight-year-old Jennifer Miller walks to school most weekdays. She lives in an apartment on the 30th floor of a skyscraper building and when she has finished breakfast and is ready to leave, she gets into the lift/elevator, descends to the ground floor and walks the two blocks to her school. When she returns in the afternoon, she takes the lift/elevator to the 25th floor and walks up the last 5 flights of stairs. She says she does not really mind doing this and she will probably go higher in the future. Why does she exit the lift/elevator on the 25th floor? She is not doing this to get more exercise, visit a friend or to lose weight.

534. A man ran into a hospital shouting *"Who shot her"*, the police arrested him on the spot. Why?

535. There was a newspaper story that a dead man's body, wearing swimming trunks, goggles and flippers, was found on a hillside that had recently been burned by a forest fire. How did the newspaper story suggest the body got there?

536. You read a strange story in a magazine article from 1962. One day a woman and her dog traveled on an old passenger train, which had no electrical services, from her village to the big city about 100 miles away. She was feeling nervous and hopeful. Halfway there, the train went through a long, dark tunnel. She stayed in the city for several days then she and her dog began the return train journey home to her village. When the train re-entered the tunnel, she burst into tears. Why?

537. Gordon Geko jumped through a window 40 floors up in the office tower block he worked in. How did he avoid being killed or injured? (He was not wearing a harness or parachute.)

538. You live midway between two big towns. To the West, town A caters more for your cultural needs and your sister lives there, it has museums and art galleries and expensive restaurants. To the East, town B has lots of shops, cafes and a good gym. A train line connects you to both. You decide to leave it to fate to choose which town to visit on Saturdays. You tell your sister you will go to the train station at a random time and catch whichever train arrives next. Both these trains visit your station every 30 minutes. After a couple of months, your sister says it is strange that she only sees you occasionally, roughly 1 in 3 Saturdays. You assure her that you have stuck to the plan. You get to the station at random times and take whichever train comes first. How can this be happening?

539. The parents of a little girl told her she must never open the cellar door. They warned her she would see things she was not meant to. One day they forgot to lock the cellar door and when they went out in their car, she opened the door. What did she see?

540. I am waiting in the lobby of an old hotel. At last, the doors of a lift/elevator open on the ground floor of the hotel. Five people get into it, including me. When the lift/elevator reaches the first floor, one person gets out and three people get in. The lift/elevator goes up to the second floor, no-one gets out but 10 people squeeze in. On the way up to the top floor, the main lift/elevator cable snaps, and it collapses down to the ground floor. Everyone who was in the elevator is badly injured except me. I did not suffer at all. How could that be?

---

541. On several different occasions over the years, people in San Francisco have reported seeing dogs driving cars, killing and injuring pedestrians. How could this happen? Why have some dogs in San Francisco been accused of reckless driving?

---

542. Two keen naturalists were out for a walk in the country. They often discussed how important it is to conserve the environment and look after wildlife. So why did one tell the other how impressed he was that he had shot an eagle?

---

543. You have been asked to solve a mystery. You are told that Caesar and Cleopatra have been found dead on the floor of a locked room. The only contents in the room are a table, a chair, a bed and some broken glass on the floor. It is mid-summer. Part of the floor is damp. Recently there was a thunderstorm and an earth tremor. The dead couple show no signs of injury, have not been poisoned, were not murdered and did not commit suicide. What has happened and how did they meet their end?

---

544. A man on a motorcycle arrives at a border crossing. Customs officers search him and find nothing suspicious. The next day the same thing happens. This goes on almost every day for weeks. The customs officials are baffled – they are convinced that the man must be smuggling something – but what? Then one of the officers has an idea when he realizes that the man always seems to cross the border the same way; they never see him make a return journey. What did the officer guess was happening?

545. A retired private eye tells you a story, from the 1970s, about a woman who suspected that her husband was having an affair. She decided to tell him that she had to go away for a few days because her mother was ill and needed her. She drove off but returned home within an hour. As she expected, her husband was not there. She went inside and was able to find out the name and address of her husband's lover within a few minutes. How did she do that?

546. Billy is an orphan. At just 3 years old, he was sent to a new home near Bricklehampton. Pete, the driver, was told the address to take him to was written on a big label tied to him. Pete stopped at a petrol station as he got close to Birmingham to check the address but was taken aback to discover that the label had gone. It had not fallen off – what happened?

547. Two old-timers (Doug and Andy) have lived next door to each other in the same apartment block for years. They are both rather frail with failing eyesight and poor hearing, but they still enjoy life and each other's company. They spend most days visiting each other, playing chess and watching sports on TV. Late one night Andy heard an unusually loud noise, he got out of bed, checked the time by looking at the old clock in the hall (it was 10:59) and opened his front door. Doug's son was leaving Doug's apartment – he said he had heard that noise too; he thought it came from upstairs and was going to investigate. Andy was horrified to discover Doug's dead body the next morning when he went to visit his old friend for his usual morning coffee. He phoned the police immediately. Doug had been shot with both barrels of one of his antique shotguns. Any fingerprints on the gun had been wiped off. The pellets had scattered and stopped the clock on Doug's wall at 11:54. The police interviewed Andy who reassured them that the only person who had visited Doug was his son, but it could not be him because he saw the son leave at 10:59, almost an hour before Doug was shot. Why did the police arrest Doug's son?

548. Cesare Borgia heard a rumor that Roderigo, his arch-enemy, was going to poison him. He went to a sorcerer and said he wanted an antidote that would save him from being poisoned. The sorcerer explained that there was no such antidote but there was a poison which would override any other. Although it was lethal by itself, when combined with any other poison it would cancel the effect of that other poison. Roderigo saw Cesare visiting the sorcerer and guessed what he might be told. He went ahead with his plan and Cesare died of poisoning 2 days later. What did Roderigo do?

549. A horrible boss named Harold was stabbed and killed in his office. The suspects are Edison, Mavis, Jason, Janie, Sofia. Before he died, Harold managed to leave a brief, cryptic message. A calendar near his body has the numbers 6, 4, 9, 10, and 11 written in blood on it. Who is the killer?

550. How did the Emperor's eldest son get revenge? A wise Emperor had 7 children, 6 of whom were extremely jealous of the eldest son, named Atticus because they thought he was the favorite. Atticus was known to be sensible and clever; he always gave his father good advice. One day the other 6 children hatched a plan to get rid of Atticus. They persuaded the royal barber to go along with this plot. When the Emperor went for his next haircut, the barber mentioned that he knew a way to communicate with ancestors but this method was so complicated and difficult that it could only be done by a very clever person. The Emperor instantly recommended his eldest son, Atticus. Atticus was told that a special fire would be lit around him and the smoke would carry him to visit heaven, that he could stay in heaven for a few days and then return home, and that chanting would protect him. If the person did not believe in the ritual or chant properly, they might not be able to return. Atticus realized immediately that this was a plan to kill him but he did not wish to annoy or disobey the emperor and agreed to perform the ritual in 2 days' time. He secretly dug a deep hole and tunnel beneath the spot the fire was built and dropped into it for a few hours once it was lit. He came out after dark and disappeared for a month. Everyone except the Emperor thought he had been burned to death. The Emperor thought he had gone to heaven to meet his ancestors and stayed there. When Atticus reappeared, he had a beard and when he was asked to talk about the Emperor's ancestors, Atticus replied he had enjoyed visiting them and that they were doing very well but were missing just one thing. What did Atticus say they were missing in heaven?

CRITICAL AND LATERAL
THINKING

551. This is a tale I was told by a world traveler (a sub-sea engineer) who claimed it is a true story. It is in 6 parts. You are invited to come up with 6 answers (the first 5 answers are provided here; the 6th is in the answers section). He said he found a strange foreign bank note on the sidewalk. Despite his many travels, he had no idea which country it was from or what currency it represented.

- Question a) What did he do? Answer a = took it to a bank and asked how much it was worth.

- Question b) Did he cash it in? Answer b = no

- Question c) What happened next? Answer c = instead of cashing it, he went to another 3 banks and asked the same question.

- Question d) What happened next? Answer = He said he was told a value ten times greater than the first bank by the 4th bank he visited.

- Question e) Did he sell the note to this 4th bank? Answer = no.

- Question f) What did he do next?

552. On another occasion, the same engineer recounted what sounded like another tall tale. He was in the big café / restaurant area of Rio de Janeiro airport waiting to be called for his flight to London. He noticed a chap a few tables away who looked really nervous. The man kept looking around him and, when two armed Brazilian police entered the room, he scarpered leaving a carrier bag on his table. Intrigued, my story teller couldn't resist getting up and checking what was in the bag. He was taken aback to find that it was stuffed with American dollars. He closed the bag quickly and returned to his seat. He started to wonder how he could smuggle this bag of money back into the UK, past customs. He would probably be jailed if he was caught and he knew that London customs officers were good at spotting people who look suspicious or as if they are hiding something. He hit on a master plan which he put into action. He claimed that it worked and that he used the money to buy a restaurant and a very fast motorbike, which he raced around the Isle of Man! What was the master plan?

553. It was a pretty normal day at work for Robert. A family doctor, GP, he was seeing patients, listening to their stories and symptoms, diagnosing, advising and prescribing. He never knew what issues, ailments and problems he would be presented with next. This morning he had 3 medical students sitting in his room, observing. He was pleased that they had been unobtrusive. He asked every patient, as they entered if they minded having these students attend the consultation. So far, everyone had agreed and carried on as it the students were not there. Robert had been voicing some of his thoughts to the students to let them understand the consultation process and get a better insight into what the job of a GP involves. The next patient, a middle-aged woman, came in and he talked about the students before asking her how he could help. She told him she had been suffering from a bad cold for over a week and was worried it might be flu. He looked at the notes he had about her and turned to the students to explain his first impressions and thinking. He said that he had not seen this patient for almost 5 years and it seemed strange that she would want to make an appointment to ask about a cold. He made a guess which turned out to be right. What did he guess?

554. Two strictly celibate monks were walking down the path from their monastery, far from civilization, high in the mountains. The path became a track beside a river. They heard a voice calling them. A woman on the other side of the river was asking for help; she was not strong enough to wade across the river. The younger monk ignored her and hurried on. The older monk crossed the river and carried her across. Hours later, the young monk could not remain silent any longer and asked *"why did you go against the teachings and carry that woman?"* What did the older monk reply?

555. This test is known as Karl Dunker's experiment. On the table in front of you, there are: two small (birthday cake type) candles, a box of matches and some drawing pins. There is a cork board hanging on the wall with some drawing pins stuck in it. Can you think of a way to attach a small candle to the corkboard on the wall so that it can be lit safely?

556. What very unusual ingredient does a Sardinian Cheese called Casu Mazu contain?

557. Two flagpoles are 50 feet high; the two ends of an 80-foot-long rope are tied to the top of these flagpoles. The rope hangs down loosely, in an arc, between them; it is so slack that at its lowest point, the rope is just 10 feet from the ground. How far apart are the flagpoles?

558. Two hundred £1 coins are spread out in front of you on a table, exactly 20 of which are heads side up. (The other 180 coins are heads down). You put on a blindfold and you are then asked if you can work out a way to create two groupings or piles of coins ensuring that each pile has equal numbers of heads-up coins. Can you do it?

559. Why is the Indiana University library sinking?

560. Six people (let's call them A D C D E and F) sat down to enjoy an all-you-can-eat buffet meal in a restaurant. A finished before B, but behind C. D finished before E but behind B. F finished before D but after B. What was the finishing order?

561. The priest of a remote village in the Pyrenees has just died, taking many confessed secrets with him. While clearing up his belongings, the women of the village discover a note that he wrote on the first day that he arrived at the village – he mentioned that he had to listen to a man who admitted being unfaithful. The note did not mention a name and there were no more notes to hint at how many more of the men had confessed to being unfaithful. The women got together and decided to make an agreement: if a woman deduces that her husband has cheated on her, she must kick him out into the street at midday the next day. This will be observed by every resident in the town. It is well known that each wife is already observant enough to know whether any man in the village (except her own husband) is cheating on his wife; however, no woman can reveal that information to any other. It is assumed that a cheating husband will remain silent about his infidelity. On the morning of the 10th day, some unfaithful men are kicked out into the street for the first time. How many of them are there?

---

562. Which of the following 4 words (Ping, Pox, Punt and Part) fits best with these 3: Peel, Pant and Potter?.

---

563. Suppose a rope was tied tightly around a sphere the same size as the Earth's equator; then an extra 3 feet was added to the length of the rope. All around the Earth sphere, the rope is raised up uniformly as high as possible to make it tight again. How high is that?

---

564. The corner of a delicious, rectangular fruit cake has been eaten. Using just one straight cut, can you cut what is left of the cake into two equal parts?

565. You have paid to go on an unusual holiday weekend at a Wild West theme park. On Saturday afternoon, you have the chance to join The Good, The Bad and The Ugly shootout game. You will be up against two famously dangerous and accurate gunmen, the Sundance Kid and Wyatt Earp. The rules of the game are that each person will have a turn to shoot one bullet (a paintball) at a time starting with the least experienced (you). Anyone hit with a paintball is effectively "dead" and no longer in the game. Last man standing is the winner. What can you do to win this game?

566. Autoland systems were designed to automate an aircraft's landing in weather conditions that would otherwise be dangerous or impossible to operate in. Early prototype versions used two cooperative software programs. The first tracked and flew down a beam that directed the aircraft on the correct flight angle decent and direction to take it to the start of the runway. If the aircraft lost the beam (for example, if it strayed above or below the beam) the safety critical software made the plane give up its decent, drop the nose and increase power to allow it to go around to start again for another try. The second program took over when the aircraft was close to the ground; the aero plane tilted back and made various adjustments in preparation for landing. What went wrong with this theory – what had not been anticipated?

567. You have been given 3 bags, each containing two hen's eggs. You are told that the first bag contains two white eggs, the second bag contains two brown eggs, and the third bag contains one white egg and one brown egg. You pick a random bag and take out one egg, which is white. What is the probability that the remaining egg from the same bag is also white?

---

568. There are two test tubes of equal capacity. In the first, there is one amoeba. In the second, there are two amoebas. An amoeba can reproduce itself in three minutes. It takes the two amoebas in the second tube 3 hours to fill the tube to capacity. How long will it take to fill the first test tube?

---

569. 250 years ago, pirates captured a small sailing boat with 3 men on board. They towed the little boat to the nearest deserted island, ate the food, drank the rum and bored with killing innocent victims, came up with a fun challenge. The 3 men are given a chance to escape with their lives. They are lined up in a row, one behind the other, and buried, in the sand of the beach, up to their necks. Trapped this way, they cannot turn around – they can only look ahead. One man can see the back of the heads of the other two, the middle man can see the back of the head of the front man, and the front man cannot see the head of either of the other two. The men are shown five hats, three of which are black and two of which are white. Next, the men are blindfolded, and one of the five hats is placed on each man's head. The remaining two hats are hidden away and then the blindfolds are removed. The men are told that if one of them can guess what color of hat he is wearing, they can all go free, but they can only have one guess! Time passes. Eventually, the man at the front, who cannot see the other two, guesses the color of his hat correctly. What color did he say it was and how did he guess correctly?

570. Why was the Fosbury Flop an example of lateral thinking?

571. Can you arrange 7 matchsticks so that they create 8 triangles?

572. Take 15 matchsticks and arrange them so that they make two rows of squares with 3 squares in the top row and 2 squares below that = 5 squares in total. The 2 lower squares should be directly below the first 2 squares of the top row. There should be no sticks below the 3rd square. You have created 5 squares. Can you remove 3 sticks and make 3 squares?

573. Take a blank sheet of paper and draw 9 dots on it so that they are arranged in a square, as 3 rows of 3, equally spaced apart. Now, can you connect them by drawing just 4 straight lines and without lifting your pen or pencil off the paper?

574. Take another blank sheet, or turn the last one over, and draw 10 small circles in a triangular shape (like the red balls at the start of a game of snooker) that is: 4 circles on the first level. 3 on the second level, 2 on the third level and one sitting on the top or apex of the triangle. (You could also do this experiment with snooker balls or oranges or coins or eggs or anything you can make a 10-piece triangle out of!). The question is: can you turn this triangle upside down by moving just 3 circles?

575. The owner of a boutique winery died recently and left 21 wine barrels to her 3 sons. Seven of the barrels are full of delicious red wine, seven barrels are half full, and seven are empty. The wine and barrels must be given to the sons equally and fairly so that each has the same number of full barrels, the same number of half-full barrels, and the same number of empty barrels. This must be done without the use of measuring devices. How can the barrels and the wine be divided equally?

576. A man is in a rowing boat on a lake; he has a brick that weighs 2 Kg and is 1 litre in volume in the boat with him. He throws the brick over the side of the boat into the water. The brick sinks quickly. The question is, does the water level in the lake go up or down?

577. The witches in Shakespeare's play "Macbeth" make an evil sounding concoction, described as: "In the cauldron boil and bake; Eye of newt and toe of frog, Wool of bat and tongue of dog, Adder's fork and blind-worm's sting, Lizard's leg and owlet's wing, For a charm of powerful trouble, Like a hell-broth boil and bubble." What are these ingredients?

578. Three people applying for a job seem equal in qualifications, skills and experience, so the prospective employer sets a problem for them to solve. He says that the job will go to the first applicant to solve it. A mark is placed on each person's forehead. The three are told that each has either a red or a blue mark. They sit facing each other. Anyone who sees a red mark on the forehead of either of the other two should raise their hand. The first one to work out what color they have on their head will get the job. All 3 people raise their hand and after a few seconds, one person comes up with the answer. What color was their mark and how did they work it out?

---

579. A young woman is whisked away to a faraway land. She kills the first person she meets. Then she teams up with three others and kills again. Can you make sense of this?

---

580. Switzerland has some beautiful mountain roads. Tourists enjoy driving along these high, winding roads and photographing the spectacular views of the Alps. Sometimes the roads go through dark tunnels. Between the tunnels, there are some fabulous viewpoints. The trouble is that lots of drivers put their headlights on to go through a tunnel but forget to switch the headlights off when they pull over into viewpoint car parks to have picnics and take photos of the spectacular scenery. All too many find their battery is so drained they cannot start the car when they return to it. To try to prevent this happening so often, authorities have spent hours discussing different strategies. Eventually, the roads authority decides to write a useful message to be displayed at the end of the tunnels but what should they write? What instructions can they give? After all, some drivers may not be stopping at viewpoints and some may not have their headlights on. What is more, if the message is too long, drivers will not have time to read it. So, what sign or message could work? Can you think of an appropriate message?

581. How did a lazy father ensure that his son reached the bus stop safely every school day?

582. A famous TV quiz show offers contestants the chance to win a car. The back wall of the TV studio has three doors. Two of the doors hide A 50-pound note and one hides the keys to a car. Contestants have to guess which door has the car behind it. The way it works is like this: each contestant makes the first selection of 1 door. The game show host then tries to tempt them away from that choice by opening one of the other two doors to show a 50-pound note. If you were the contestant, would you stick with your first choice or take the option to go for the other closed door?

583. What did a man from Chicago do, in 2007 to try to avoid paying a $175 fine to a phone service provider?

584. A scientist is conducting a series of research experiments aimed at testing aspects of primate intelligence. One morning he brings a chimpanzee into a cage that has a delicious looking bunch of bananas dangling from a hook in the middle of the ceiling. The cage is a cube, 3 meters wide, by 3 meters long, by 3 meters high. The cage is empty but for three reinforced cardboard boxes lying on the floor. Each of these boxes is almost 1 meter high and they are shaped so that they can be stacked. The scientist starts his stopwatch and begins to observe and record the chimp's actions. The chimp is quick to work out a way to get the bananas but does not act as the scientist expected. What did the chimp do? How did the chimp reach the bananas? (The chimp did not try to jump that high or climb the walls of the cage).

---

585. Once Upon a time, in a faraway land, a powerful King, who does not want his daughter (the Princess) to get married, makes every suitor do a test. Before the test starts, the king leads each Princely candidate to the middle of a big courtyard that is covered in black and white pebbles. A circle of courtiers stands around the edge of the courtyard to watch. The king announces that he is going to reach down to the ground, pick up one white and one black pebble and put them into a velvet bag. To prove their worth, the hopeful Prince must put his hand into the bag and choose the white pebble. Everyone who fails to select the white pebble is expelled from the kingdom and told never to return. After many have tried and failed, the next Prince arrives. As the test begins, this Prince notices that the King has surreptitiously picked up, and put into the bag, two black pebbles. He knows he cannot accuse the king of cheating. What can he do?

---

586. Which came first, the chicken or the egg?

---

587. A delivery van driver who refuses to pay a speeding and failing to stop fine is summoned to court. His defense is that he is deaf and he did not realize that an unmarked police car had followed him on a country road for 3 miles with its siren blaring loudly. He had written a note to say that he is prepared to pay the speeding fine but as he is deaf, he did not know the police were demanding that he slow down and pull over, so cannot be accused of failing to stop. He wrote that he cannot answer any questions in court unless he is assigned a sign-language translator. The prosecution lawyer has an idea, he meets the sign-language translator before she comes into the courtroom and she agrees to the plan. Within an hour, the van driver is prosecuted for failing to stop, for perjury and for wasting the court's time. What did the lawyer say to the translator?

---

588. A friend invites you to visit the old house he has just bought. It needs a lot of renovation work and the electrical wiring is quaint, to say the least! Standing in one of the corridors, he is about to show you an example of this when he changes his mind and says *"I bet you cannot figure this out! I'll buy lunch if you can do it."* He shows you three light switches on the wall outside a room. The room's door is closed (it fits tightly so you cannot tell if the light is on when the door is shut), you cannot see in to the room at all. He explains that only one of these switches turns on the center ceiling light; the other two switches are spares and do nothing. He challenges you to work out a way to tell which switch turns the light on. You are not allowed to unlock and open the door until you have decided what to do and told him your plan (you cannot peek in). Can you think of a way to achieve this?

---

589. Why did LaMarcus Adna Thompson invent, patent and build the Switchback Gravity Railway roller coaster for visitors to Brooklyn's Coney Island in 1884?

---

590. The governor of a prison offers 100 death row prisoners a chance to avoid execution. The prisoners are numbered from 1 to

100. He tells them that there is a room which contains a wall cupboard with 100 drawers. He has put one number, from 1 to 100, in each drawer, in a random way. The prisoners will be allowed to enter the room, one after another. Each prisoner may open and look into 50 drawers in any order. The drawers are closed again afterwards. If, during this search, every prisoner finds their number in one of the drawers, all prisoners are pardoned. If even one prisoner does not find their number, all prisoners remain on death row. Before the first prisoner enters the room, the prisoners may discuss and plan a strategy but may not communicate once the first prisoner enters to look in the drawers. What is the prisoners' best strategy?

591. You are driving down a country road, in your 2-seater sports car, on a freezing cold, stormy evening when you pass a bus stop and see three people waiting for a bus. (You have a small snow shovel, a rope, a flask of hot coffee and a blanket in the car.) An old lady who looks like she is about to die of cold; a good friend who once saved your life when you were on an expedition together and the perfect partner you always dreamed of (your soul mate). Knowing that your car can only take one passenger, what would you do?

592. What catastrophic mistake did the captain of a navy destroyer ship make when out at sea testing a new torpedo guidance software program? The software amendment was added as a precaution, a fail-safe in case the torpedo went out of control and turned back in the direction of the ship that launched it. This software was designed to trigger the torpedo to self-destruct (blow itself up) if it turned more than 180 degrees from the direction it was fired in.

593. You are enrolled as a university student on an environmental sciences degree. A field study coursework requires you to collect evidence of pollution levels in a city 50 miles away. You are given a glass beaker container with a tight-fitting lid. You are concerned that you are likely to contaminate the sample you want to collect with the air already in the beaker, which would ruin the accuracy of the measurement. How can you be sure of retrieving a representative sample of the city air?

594. The Suspect's or Prisoner's Dilemma is a thought experiment that offers two suspected criminals a choice: they can refuse to implicate the other criminal or betray them. They can opt for altruism and partnership or selfishness and disloyalty. Trust and cooperation will reduce their jail sentences. Betrayal will benefit one but not the other unless they both betray (defect) in which case they both suffer a longer jail sentence. Tony and Bob are arrested and put in solitary confinement. They cannot communicate. The crime they have committed carries a maximum sentence of 10 years in prison, but since the police are not certain of getting both Tony and Bob convicted, they are prepared to give them a sentence of just 2 years. The chance of conviction would be far more certain if one of the men could be persuaded to betray the other man. If one of them confesses to the crime and betrays the other, they will avoid prison and can go free on probation, leaving the other to serve the full sentence. So, there are 4 possible outcomes:

- If Tony and Bob both stay silent, they will each serve 2 years in prison.

- If Tony betrays Bob and Bob stays silent, Tony will be set free while Bob serves 10 years in prison.

- If Bob betrays Tony and Tony stays silent, Bob will be set free and Tony will serve 10 years in prison.

- If Tony and Bob betray each other, they share the 10-year sentence and serve 5 years each.

The Prisoner's Dilemma poses questions about friendship, loyalty and rational behaviour and is used in game theory. If you were Tony or Bob, what do you think your best strategy is – stay silent or betray?

---

595. Said to have been created by Albert Einstein when he was a boy (although there is little evidence of this), the Zebra Puzzle is claimed to be so difficult that only 2% of the population can solve it. There are several versions of the puzzle; the one below is based on a version published in Life International magazine on December 17, 1962; the solution was published in the March 25, 1963, issue of Life.

- There are five houses.

- The Englishman lives in the red house.

- The Spaniard owns the dog.

- Coffee is drunk in the greenhouse.

- The Ukrainian drinks tea.

- The greenhouse is immediately to the right of the ivory house.

- The Old Gold smoker owns snails.

- Kools are smoked in the yellow house.

- Milk is drunk in the middle house.

- The Norwegian lives in the first house.

- The man who smokes Chesterfields lives in the house next to the man with the fox.

- Kools are smoked in the house next to the house where the horse is kept.

- The Lucky Strike smoker drinks orange juice.

- The Japanese smokes Parliaments.

- The Norwegian lives next to the blue house.

- Each of the houses is painted a different color and their inhabitants are of different national extractions, own different pets, drink different drinks and smoke different brands of cigarettes.

So, who drinks water? Who owns the zebra?

---

596. A physics lecturer gave a student a very low mark for the answers she gave to an examination question. The lecturer said she had not taken the question seriously and had been flippant. The student complained and claimed she should have been awarded an A grade. She argued that she had gone way beyond what was asked for by writing 6 answers that were all theoretically valid. The exam question was: "Explain how someone could determine the height of a tall building with the aid of a barometer." How many answers can you think of? Can you do what the student did and provide up to 6 different answers to this question?

---

597. It seemed that the two lifts/elevators in a tall office block did not work sufficiently well. People complained that they were getting frustrated and annoyed because it often took ages for a lift to arrive, especially at certain times of the day. What can be done to improve things and reduce complaints? From a critical/lateral thinking perspective, there could be many ways of dealing with this situation. How many can you come up with? There are 20 listed in the answers at the back of the book. (Hint: consider carefully what the problem to be solved is. Feel free to brainstorm and be imaginative and don't worry too much about practicalities and feasibility).

---

598. It can be interesting to think about, and play with, views and explanations of something's purpose, it's reason for being. For example the purpose of a book might be; to amuse; to entertain; to help you pass the time on a long journey; to motivate and inspire change; to provide sources of poetry and mantras; to give you something to help you fall asleep; to offer guidance and recipes; to provide certain important facts and definitions; to fire the imagination; to discuss philosophy; to preach; to explain a version or interpretation of history; to satirize; to keep you guessing; to preserve certain knowledge and language; to inform; to misinform; ,,,,. The main purpose of a prison may be to rehabilitate, to punish or to lock people away from society – each of those intentions or purposes produces a different type of prison. So, what might be the purpose of a cat? A cat is a system to _____? How many can you think of?

---

599. Try the same stimulating thought exercise exploring views of the purposes, roles, and functions of dogs and horses.

600. Finally, a question that has no correct answer. It is a conundrum. An ethical dilemma. It is up to each one of us to consider the implications of this question and think about what we would do if presented with a similar situation. While it is a rather extreme example, this story or scenario has echoes in many aspects of daily life. To what extent should we help people? What can we do to assist those who are starving and in poor health? Should we eat animals? Could we do more about climate change?

The Case Study: A runaway train is careering down the railway track at great speed. Five people are tied to the track, unable to move. The train is heading straight for them. You are standing next to a lever that operates a track change. If you pull this lever, the train will go in a different direction and switch to a different set of tracks; it will not hit the 5 people. One person is on the other track. The question you need to bear in mind is that if you do pull the lever, the train will certainly avoid the 5 but hit the one person on the other track. You have two options:

- Do nothing, in which case the runaway train will kill the five people on the main track.

- Pull the lever, diverting the runaway train onto a side track where it will kill one person.

What would you do? Would you have the desire, fortitude, confidence or is it courage to pull the lever? On the other hand, would you decide not to intervene, to as it were, turn your back. After all, it is not your problem; you are not responsible for this; you were just out for a walk. If you pull the lever, you are sealing the fate of the person on the other track, you will have deliberately caused that person to die (to save 5 others) and you will need to live with that thought for the rest of your life (reassuring yourself that you saved 5). What would they say in court if this event ever went that far? Could someone argue that you murdered the person on the alternate track? Are you ready to live with the implications of the court decision and the potential/likely feelings of guilt of being responsible for killing that person? But, looking at it a different way, you can reassure yourself that, by taking that action you saved the 5 people on the other track. Which is the more ethical option? What is the right thing to do? Maybe we should turn to a philosopher to help us make his momentous decision. Immanuel Kant might say that we must not kill anyone – that we must live by our principles. John Stuart Mill and Jeremy Bentham would argue for the greatest good of the greatest number; they might say that it is clear that we should save 5 people even if we have to sacrifice one person to achieve this. What we have not taken into account so far are confusing factors that are likely to influence our decision. For example, suppose we hate or love one of the people on the track, isn't that very likely to affect and bias our thinking? Does critical and or lateral thinking help in this case?

ANSWERS!#?

EASY, FUN, STARTER QUESTIONS

1. Stop imagining! (Or imagine turning the light on).

2. Cows drink Water

3. All months have 28 days.

4. A greenhouse is made of wood or aluminum and glass or plastic.

5. John.

6. One spiral groove.

7. "How long"

8. This man did not want to step on the cracks.

9. Mummy bulls do not exist.

10. You take away two and you have 2 apples.

11. How can you divide 2 pizzas equally among 3 people – make three side-to-side cake or pie cuts in each, producing 2 times 6 pieces.

12. They weigh the same – (but I think a ton of stones would hurt me far more than a ton of feathers if they landed on me!)

13. Yesterday, today, and tomorrow.

14. The pile-up accident was caused by a child playing with toy cars; the cars fell out of their box and tumbled downstairs.

15. A towel gets wetter as it dries.

16. The man handed over a note asking the bank teller for cash from his account.

17. You are the driver – how old are you?

18. Cats (like all creatures) have one birthday.

19. The barman guessed that the best way to stop the man's hiccups was to give him a fright.

20. Same as the speed of sound = 740 mph.

21. Footsteps, footprints are what is left behind.

22. The man is serving in the navy on a submarine; he will claim the prize when he returns home.

23. The bullets will reach the ground at the same moment.

24. There are 4 errors.

25. You should light the match first.

26. Harold crashed into a car transporter.

27. Push the cork into the bottle and shake the ring out.

28. Mr. Lyon recognized that Lucy's mouse was on its last legs. He had several healthy mice in the back room so he selected the one that looked like Lucy's and gave that one to her.

29. What are you bound to find in the middle of Toronto? = an O

30. The book was a paperback.

31. Keep your word

32. They were making a movie and the accident was a stunt.

33. Charcoal.

34. The other end of the rope was not tied to anything so the horse could wander around dragging the rope behind it.

35. Why was the personal assistant walking down the long driveway to get the mail / post? The post is not delivered on Sundays.

36. A hovercraft.

37. Second place

38. He was a priest (a preacher) conducting weddings.

39. A deck of cards

40. He was confident because sommeliers do not swallow wine when they taste it – they spit it out.

41. Seven

42. The woman dropped her contact lens into the soup and does not want to swallow it.

43. The pilot was in a flight simulator.

44. The gangster's car was parked in the middle of a big, outdoor, drive-in movie theatre and everyone had been watching a war film full of loud explosions and gunfire.

45. Nine

46. Mum and daughter are visiting a zoo.

47. The other person was probably playing tennis.

48. The judge threw the case out because the thief did not take the helmet off so could not be identified.

49. He said, "*You will hang me.*"

50. The husband had taken the car to the automatic car wash.

LOGIC

51. Switch 1 = Up, 2 = Middle, 3 = Down.

52. Because 1984 bottles are about 40 more than 1939 bottles, the bottles each cost the same.

53. Answer = (from left to right) 7 of diamonds, 10 of spades, 8 of hearts and 9 of clubs.

54. Throw the ball straight up vertically.

55. Next two letters are A W. They are the first letters of the words in the sentence "What are the next two letters in the following series and why? (The first letters of the words in the question).

56. The single question you should ask is *"If I was to ask the other person where the car is what would they say?"* The liar will lie about what the truth teller would say and point the wrong way, the truth teller knows the other person will lie and also point the wrong way.

57. Mary has 8 or more sons. Mary has less than 8 sons. Mary has at least 1 son. If only one of these statements is true, Mary must have NO sons.

58. Counterfeit notes answer = 2 checks. a) split the 15 notes into 4 piles of: 4, 4, 4 and 3. Place each of the piles of 4 into different slots in the machine. If the alarm does not go off on any of the slots, you know the counterfeit must be in the pile of 3. b) take the pile with the fake note in it and place one

note in each of the slots. If the alarm does not go off, it must be the 4th note.

59. Put the dog in the canoe, row to the other side, drop the dog off and return. Collect one sheep, row across, drop it off and collect the dog. Drop the dog off on the first bank and collect the second sheep. Row it across, drop it off then return to get the dog.

60. Take the goat across and leave it, row back, collect the hay take it to the other bank and swap it with the goat, i.e., bring the goat back, drop the goat off, collect the leopard and drop it off on the other side (with the hay). Row back and collect the goat.

61. Yemen (Catch me if **Y**ou can)

62. You could get the dog to follow you and circle the tree it is tied to; the rope will get shorter as it circulates.

63. Their uncle told them to jump onto the other person's bicycle and race to the finish.

64. To avoid being burnt, you could move quickly to the middle of the island and start another fire that will burn off the dry vegetation at that end of the island and form a fire break.

65. You could tell which water came from which jug if the water in one jug was frozen.

66. Why would the man knock if he thought it was his room?

67. This phenomenon was observed when the seat-belt wearing law was introduced; it was proposed that the main reason was because more people were surviving car accidents. People who wore seat belts when they had car accidents were more likely to be injured and not die than previously - in the days before they wore seat belts.

68. The man who overslept was a lighthouse keeper and a there was shipwreck because the light had not been switched on.

69. They stood the signpost back up again and pointed the arrow with the name of the village they stayed the night in towards the direction they had just come from – allowing them to see which way to go next.

70. Frank was laundering cash – he was getting rid of counterfeit notes – the trouble is the cashier might give him back the notes he gave her.

71. The man was a lion tamer; he forgot the chair he always used.

72. The car is called Lizzy.

73. The suggestion was to let some air out of the tires so that the height of the truck went down enough to get through.

74. The river was frozen, Lucca crossed the river by running over the ice.

75. The so-called village idiot was smart enough to realize that as long as he kept choosing the £1-coin, people would keep offering him the choice. If he started taking the £10 note, the donations would stop.

76. The best strategy in this card game would be: the first player turns over the top card (which cannot be the joker as it is in the pack) then, when they sneak a peek at the next three cards, if they see three ordinary cards, they should turn the top two cards over – the next person will know that the next card is safe – they can turn the next card over and sneak a look at the next three and so on. If they see one ordinary card and the joker 2nd, they turn over the top one and the next player knows to ask you to take the next turn. If the joker is

at the top, they turn no cards over and the next person tells you it is your turn.

77. Tell your friend to leave one pistachio on the floor and when the nut person comes in, ask him if he knows what this strange thing is and whether it is edible.

78. Do not allow yourself to be tempted to open the beginning and end of each little chain, instead open all the rings in one chain (ie just 4 rings) and use them to link the other chains together.

79. The man should wind the grandfather and set it to 12 o'clock, then walk to the village, read the time on the church clock and walk back home at the same speed. He will then look at the time on the grandfather clock and divide the time he has been away by 2 (assuming the journey to the village took the same amount of time as the journey home), add that to the time on the church clock and reset the grandfather clock to the correct time.

80. The third envelope.

Assumptions

81. It is a toy train set in someone's house.

82. No – if he is alive, she is not a widow. A widow is a woman whose spouse has died, the man in question would have to be deceased for this scenario to make sense, and if he is deceased, then he cannot get married.

83. The window cleaner was standing cleaning the inside of the windows on the 30th floor – he fell on the floor.

84. A chess game.

85. We do not bury survivors!

86. No real coin would be dated BC (before Christ).

87. It is a Volkswagen Beetle.

88. Stan is playing baseball – on a home run towards the catcher.

89. Chances are the water in the second bucket is frozen.

90. The man may have been sent out as a distraction or decoy for the police – to act or pretend to be drunk so that the police would follow him and that would allow someone else who was worried about being breathalyzed to go while the police were away.

91. When the 2 planes meet, neither will be closer to Lisbon – at that moment, they are exactly the same distance from Lisbon.

92. Children visiting Santa / Father Christmas.

93. Well, the story goes that the two men were marooned on a deserted island after the ship they were in was wrecked on a reef in a storm. They were the only survivors and they washed up on different beaches. The first man established a rudimentary camp, built a shelter and a campfire and started cooking meat. When the second man found him, he was grateful to have some food and when he asked where the meat came from, the first man said he caught a turtle. The second man however, always suspected he may have been eating one of the other ship passengers. As soon as he tasted the turtle, he knew that was not what the meat he had eaten on the island tasted like.

94. The King, a Queen, and two twins are beds

95. The two golfers were playing tennis.

96. She was playing Monopoly.

97. The second room - a tiger that has not eaten for a year is likely to be dead!

98. The surgeon is the man's wife and the boy's mother.

99. The shiny black car is a hearse and it had a coffin in it.

100.   June only has 30 days.

101.   Sally is a dog and she knows the big dog well – they often play together.

102.   Mr Burton was a billionaire – he is giving his money away and will become is a millionaire.

103.   The bear is white – you are at the North Pole and so it must be a polar bear.

104.   The young driver could see the ninja easily because it was the middle of the day and the sun was shining.

105. The man was giving mouth-to-mouth resuscitation to a woman who had collapsed in the street.

106. I am a cleaner who regularly wipes surfaces.

107. Arthur is a cat.

108. It is Halloween and he was out going around the neighborhood, being given gifts.

109. The cleverest ones pull the bath plug out!

110. She was walking.

TRIVIA

111. The wife carrying world championships have been held in Sonkajärvi, Finland, every year since 1992. The prize is the wife's weight in beer.

112. 22 months

113. Apparently, you might eat around 70 assorted insects and 10 spiders or more.

114. Switzerland is number 1 (19.4 pounds per capita), then Germany (17.8 pounds), Ireland (17.4 pounds), UK (16.8 pounds), and Sweden (14.6 pounds).

115. The longest wedding veil ever created was an astonishing 6,962.6 meters worn by Maria Paraskeva.

116. "Gardyloo" is an archaic Scottish expression meaning "*Look out below*", shouted just before people threw the contents of their chamber pots out of the window.

117. Golf.

118. A type of energy drink! – it was the sports drink chosen by Roman charioteers because they thought it improved their performance in the arena.

119. This Burgundy sold for $558,000. The bottle of 1945 Romanee-Conti sold at Sotheby for more than 17 times its original estimate of $32,000.

120. Marie Curie was the first woman to win a Nobel Prize.

121. The Dragon's Breath chili pepper is so hot it can be deadly, it could cause a type of anaphylactic shock, burning your airways and closing them up.

122. The shortest flight is Loganair's return service between Westray (population = 600) and Papa Westray (population = 90) – two of the Orkney Isles, which are 1.7 miles apart. The flight takes 90 seconds.

123. Indonesia banned hula hoops because they "might stimulate passion."

124. Koalas have fingerprints.

125. Bermuda features a shipwreck on its national flag.

126. The odds of getting a royal flush are about 650,000 to 1; (a straight flush = over 70,000 to 1).

127. They bought two large Papa John's pizzas that cost about $30 at the time.

128. Saturn has 82 moons.

129. Henry the VIII made Valentine's Day a holiday in 1537.

130. It is illegal to swear near a dead person in Texas.

131. Greenland sharks live at least 250 years, maybe 500.

132. 76 hot dogs in 10 minutes!

133. Lobsters communicate with their urine.

134. You can still stay at the world's oldest spa and hotel – the Nishiyama Onsen Keiunkan in Japan, founded in 705 AD.

135. Hippopotamus milk is pink.

136. Drivers spend about 2 weeks of their lives waiting at traffic lights? Furthermore, during an average lifetime, most

people spend a year sitting on the toilet and around a quarter of a million hours sleeping.

137.   Mary Shelley was 18 when she wrote Frankenstein.

138.   Cocaine is present in 90% of American dollars.

139.   Giant pandas eat about 5 tons of bamboo per year.

140.   About 700 grapes go into one bottle of wine (over 2 kilos).

141.   Ferdinand Magellan named the Pacific Ocean.

142.   12 languages are written from right to left.

143.   Playboy was the first to trademark their service uniforms in the U.S.A.

144.   A dog's sense of smell is about 40 times more powerful than a human's — they have 300 million olfactory receptors. Dogs also have neophilia, which means they are attracted to new and interesting smells.

145.   Alfred Hitchcock suffered from ovophobia, a horror of eggs. He told a journalist, "*I'm frightened of eggs, worse than frightened – they revolt me. That white round thing without any holes, and when you break it, inside there's that yellow thing, round, without any holes…*"

146.   Hair grows about 6 inches (15 centimeters) per year, on average.

147.   A pufferfish (fugu) is more poisonous than cyanide. Fugu has been consumed in Japan and Korea for more than 2500 years, possibly as long as 8000 years.

148.   The original "purpose" of "goosebumps" was to ward off predators.

149. British soldiers had to make do with a daily ration of 3 sheets of toilet paper; Americans were allocated 22.

150. A flock of crows is called a murder.

151. A tsunami wave can travel at over 500mph in the deep ocean, a tsunami can move as fast as a jet, and its wavelength, the distance from crest to crest, may be hundreds of miles.

152. Japan

153. A bat can eat 3,000 mosquitos per night.

154. 25% of Americans believe that Sherlock Holmes was a real person.

155. The oldest-known living land animal was born in 1832; he is a tortoise named Jonathan, who has lived on the island of St. Helena in the Atlantic Ocean since 1882.

156. Mickeys per second.

157. Honey

158. Dolly Parton, what's more, she lost to a drag queen and, true to her style, she often tells the story.

159. King Solomon reputedly had 700 wives and 300 concubines.

160. The first ice hockey pucks were made of cow dung.

161. We blink around 20 times per minute. You can blink up to 5 times per second if you try, which makes the eyes the fastest muscle in the body.

162. The legend of the Loch Ness monster is about 1500 years old.

163. "Alice in Wonderland syndrome" is a condition that makes people feel larger or smaller than they really are.

164. You are not allowed to tease skunks in Minnesota.

165. Greece has a national anthem with 158 verses.

166. Hippopotomostrosesquippedaliophobia is the fear of long words (rather silly to give it such a long name! or was that deliberate?).

167. The total weight of all the ants in the world is about the same as the total weight of all the humans.

168. A crocodile cannot stick out its tongue.

169. Walter Arnold was caught zooming through Paddock Wood in Kent at a terrifying 8 mph in 1896.

170. The feet of the central figure in the painting (fresco) were cut off when a door was installed in the wall beneath the fresco.

171. There are 28 dominos in a set and 168 dots altogether.

172. An octopus has 3 hearts.

173. The coldest temperature ever recorded on Earth was almost minus 100 Celsius (-144 degrees Fahrenheit, -98 degrees Celsius).

174. The unicorn is the national animal of Scotland; a unicorn was first featured on the Scottish royal coat of arms in the 12th century.

175. A group of unicorns is called a blessing.

176. An ostrich's eye is bigger than its brain.

177. A 5000-year-old Stone Age piece of chewing gum was found by an archaeology student in Finland; it was made from birch bark tar and still had tooth impressions.

178. 259 minutes

179.   John Paul Getty, one of the richest men in the world, installed payphones and dial-locks on the normal phones in his house.

180.   Which is longer on the planet Venus – a year or a day? Answer = a day! It takes 225 Earth days for Venus to orbit the sun but it takes Venus 243 days to rotate on its axis, so a Venus day is longer than a year!

181.   Over 2,000,000

182.   The "sixth sick sheik's sixth sheep's sick".

183.   Your brain uses up around 20 percent of your body's blood and oxygen.

184.   3 countries that do not use the metric system = Liberia, Myanmar, and the United States.

185.   The jaw has the strongest muscle in the human body.

186.   Almost all commercially grown artichokes (99.9 percent) come from California.

187.   2 rats could have over million descendants.

188.   J. Edgar Hoover banned people from walking on his shadow.

189.   About 69% of the world's freshwater is held in ice sheets, glaciers and permanent snow. (Will it last?)

190.   Walt Disney was afraid of mice.

191.   4, the Danube flows through Vienna, Bratislava, Budapest, and Belgrade.

192.   A study found that surgeons who play video games at least 3 hours a week perform 27% faster and make 37% fewer

errors performing laparoscopic surgery than their colleagues who did not play video games.

193.   It is said to be illegal for a single woman to skydive in Florida on Sundays.

194.   Nicaragua and Dominica include the color purple in their national flags.

195.   12% of the world's population is over 60 years of age? (52% are under 30).

196.   Researchers from the University of Vienna gathered 947 hours of giraffe noises, over 8 years, at 3 zoos and discovered that they produced a humming sound at night to help to keep their herd together in poor light.

197.   The tallest building in the world is the Burg Khalifa in Dubai; it is over 828 meters (2,716 feet) high.

198.   It is illegal to wake bears up in Alaska.

199.   The largest monetary treasure haul was found in the sea near Gibraltar, in 2007, on the wreck named Black Swan. The salvage team reportedly found 17 tons of coins valued at $500 million, an amount that is both staggering and thought to be unprecedented in the treasure-hunting world.

200.   The best longbows, made of yew that may have required a force of 150 to 180 pounds (70 to 80 kg) to pull back the drawstring fully could shoot arrows 300 yards (almost 1,000 feet) depending on the weight of the arrow. While not very accurate at that distance, the longbow can shoot through soldiers' armor at a range of 250 yards. It is thought that each bowman carried 60 to 70 arrows.

201.   Vincent van Gogh sold just one painting while he was alive (his paintings are worth over £100,000,000 now).

202.   Buckingham Palace has 78 bathrooms (more than twice as many as the White House in Washington, DC).

203.   Roast camel is the largest menu item in the world. It is served as a whole camel that is stuffed with lamb that has been stuffed with chickens, the chickens are stuffed with fish or eggs. Several stages of stuffing also include rice or other ingredients mixed in.

204.   Love, the story goes that the 3 goddesses - Aphrodite, Athena, and Hera - fought over who was the fairest. They asked prince Paris of Troy to judge and throw an apple at the most beautiful goddess (Aphrodite won).

205.   Ferrari, Porsche, Ford Mustang.

206.   Pink toilet paper.

207.   2 countries that do not allow tattoos are Iran and Japan. Iran has also outlawed spiky haircuts and sunbeds as signs of devil worship. In Japan, tattoos are associated with members of organized crime syndicates.

208.   The world's fastest bird is the Peregrine Falcon.

209.   2,700,000 towels are stolen from Holiday Inns per year in the USA.

210.   Crocodile dung was once used as a contraceptive. Ancient Egyptian women mixed crocodile dung with sour milk.

211.   The Niagara Falls are about 7 miles from where they started. The cascading water has eroded the falls back upriver.

212.   83 aircraft - capable of carrying more than 14 passengers and where no trace (bodies or debris) has ever been found - have been declared "missing" since 1948, according to data compiled by the Aviation Safety Network.

213. Because of food sources and EU regulations. All the good animal carcasses are on the 'Spanish' side of the border. Both the griffon vulture (Gyps fulvus) and the black vulture (Aegypius monachus) can fly hundreds of miles in search of carrion to eat, yet it is clear that they avoid Portuguese territory. The climate, topography, and ecosystems on either side of the border are similar, but a 2001 EU directive to curb mad cow disease mandated the immediate burial or incineration of cattle found dead in fields. Spain, which is home to 9 out of 10 of Europe's carrion bird population, abandoned the measure a few years later, but the directive is still in place in Portugal.

214. It takes 70 different pieces of wood to make a violin.

215. Apparently, it is illegal to sing in public places in Florida if you are wearing a swimming costume. What is more – it is illegal to sing out of tune in North Carolina; the law dates back to the 19th century when a man was fined for singing loudly and out of tune in Lumberton.

216. Sauna culture in Finland is an integral part of the lives of most of the population. Finnish people believe that saunas are relaxing - the heat (sometimes over 100 Celsius) – is thought to be good for calming the mind and encouraging a sense of inner peace. Saunas raise heart rate, allow blood vessels to dilate, and increase blood flow to the skin.

217. The tip or end of a whip. The crack a whip makes is produced when a section of the whip moves faster than the speed of sound, creating a small sonic boom.

218. Because Guinea pigs need social interaction, they live in groups and are very communicative in their natural habitat.

219.   The inaugural Westfield Sydney to Melbourne 544 mile Ultramarathon was won by Cliff Young, an Australian potato farmer, then aged 61. He competed in overalls and work boots without his dentures - saying that they rattled when he ran. He ran at a slow, loping pace and trailed a long way behind the pack at first but kept going when the other competitors stopped to sleep. He ran continuously for five days, taking the lead during the first night and eventually winning by 10 hours. He said he had previously run in gumboots for two to three days in a row rounding up sheep and that during the race, he imagined he was herding sheep and trying to outrun a storm. When he was awarded the prize of A$10,000, he explained that he had not known there was a prize and that he felt bad accepting it as the other five finishers had worked as hard as he did. He split the money equally between them, keeping none. Cliff Young became famous and popular after this "tortoise and hare" feat and was awarded the Medal of the Order of Australia in 1984.

220.   Hans (Dolph) Lundgren has appeared in over 80 films, speaks 5 languages, has undergraduate and Master's degrees in chemical engineering, won a scholarship to MIT, holds the rank of 4th dan black belt in karate, becoming European champion in 1980–81, and was a bodyguard for Grace Jones.

Playing With Words

221.   SHORT

222.   Envelope

223.   Tree

224.   QUEUE

225.   Writing the words in a grid below each other and then reading down the 7 columns vertically gives: 'Why did the chicken cross the road'.

226.   The longest one-syllable word in the English language is "scraunched", "screeched" comes second.

227.   The word is HEROINE

228.   Cats, all the others, when spelled backward, are words.

229.   Norwegian wood, Italian job, Maltese falcon, Greek yogurt, Portuguese man o'war, Cuban heels, Swedish chef, Scots guards, Dutch courage, Spanish fly, French connection, German shepherd, Irish stew, Turkish delight

230.   WRONG

231.   They all look the same in a mirror or flipped horizontally.

232.   Eye, hip, arm, leg, ear, toe, rib, lip, gum, jaw.

233.   They are all anagrams of UK nations' plants: rose = England, leek = Wales, shamrock = Ireland and thistle = Scotland – the last of which is also an anagram of the list.

234.   Heartache and headache.

235.   tern, ox, owl, lion, vole, bat, gnat, cow, crow, panda, raven.

236.   Kayak, radar, refer.

237.   Eat / ate

238.   Chad, Finland, Iran, Oman, Spain. B-olivia and G-reece

239.   NOON, OXO, SWIMS.

240.   Suns

241.   You can replace the letter a with an e

242.   Wheat, Heat, Eat, Tea.

243.   Dreamt

244.   STARTLING (which means surprising) is the only 9 letter word in the English language that gives another word every time you remove a letter from it. Startling, starting, staring, string, sting, sing, sin, in, I.

245.   Deer throws is an anagram of three words.

246.   Strengths.

247.   Anagrams: 1) astronomers are moon starters; 2) the Statue of Liberty was built to stay free; 3) be silent and listen; 4) the eyes THEY SEE

248.   Tremendous, horrendous, stupendous, and hazardous.

249.   Portuguese

250.   If you take the first letter of each of these words and place it at the end, it will spell the same word backwards: revive, banana, grammar, voodoo, assess, potato, dresser, uneven.

RIDDLES

251. A Sponge

252. A pearl.

253. Your name

254. Your Grandma clicked (shot) a photo of him with an old fashioned 35mm film camera. Then she placed his photo in a liquid for five minutes to develop the image, then hung her husband's photo, which is the final step in developing an image (drying the photograph).

255. An option.

256. A candle

257. Light

258. Your breath.

259. The day before tomorrow is today, two days after today and one day before is equal to tomorrow, which is given to be Friday, so tomorrow is Friday and therefore today is Thursday, OR another way to explain it is: the day before tomorrow is today, one-day before is yesterday and two days after yesterday is tomorrow, which is given to be Friday, so tomorrow is Friday which means today is Thursday.

260. Richard is buying individual numbers to put on the front door of his house; he bought 3 (the number 100) and paid £2 for each digit.

261. An anchor

262. A river

263. The horizon

264. A shirt

265. A Boxing ring

266. A match stick

267. Water, Chemical formulae: $CO_2 + C_2H_4O_2 + C_6H_6O - C_9H_8O_4 = H_2O$

268. Paint is wet when you put it on.

269. She had triplets.

270. Your shadow

271. TeapoT

272. Advice.

273. A blacksmith shoeing horses

274. Both sentences contain all the letters of the alphabet (a to z); the second is slightly shorter than the first.

275. squash

276. A secret

277. The Big Ben clock tower in London has 4 sides so 8 hands.

278. A glove.

279. A mirror

280. Mercury

281. the words TON and NOT.

282. Vowels (the words "a tennis court" include all 5 vowels)

283. Make apple sauce!

284. Temper

285. A bank has branches but no fruit, trunk or leaves.

286. Painless operation. The letters missing in O_ER _T _O_ (OPERATION) spell out PAIN. Thus, "painless" operation.

287. A fence

288. Your left elbow

289. Push

290. He is a barber.

291. An echo.

292. Kiwi

293. A golf ball.

294. Night and day.

295. a thumb

296. Three. (1 2) 3 1 (2 3) 1 (2) 3

297. A ping pong / table tennis ball.

298. A coffin

299. The letter M.

300. Tug of War.

Numbers

301.　Turn it upside down and around to get 81 = 9 x 9.

302.　1 minute

303.　The number 8549176320 is special because the numbers are in alphabetic order – eight, five, four, nine, one, seven, …

304.　The snail will reach the top in 28 days- it reaches the top of the well and does not slide back.

305.　Separate the coins into 3 piles, 2 sets of 3 and 1 set of 2. Weigh the 2 sets of 3 and compare them – if they weigh the same, put them to one side and weigh the remaining two and select the heavier. If the 2 sets of 3 are different weights, choose whichever side is heavier, take 2 of those coins and compare them – if they are different, you can see which is the heavier; if they weigh the same, it must be the 3rd coin – i.e. the one you did not weigh.

306.　1 2 3

307.　Place the two fuses side by side. Light them and as soon as the 2-minute fuse is burnt, the other will have 4 minutes left.

308.　7

309.　Not only do they both add up to 13 but they also contain the same letters – they are anagrams.

310.　Adding hours on a clock.

311.　78 seconds, the last cut will produce 2 pieces.

312.   CADAEIBFEC might be code for the start of the number Pi = 3.1415…

313.   Hint: (2^ (2*2+2))-2/2. Answer = 63

314.   £12,000. (6/12th to you, 3/12th to the godson, 2/12th to his friend = 11/12th so the £1,000 must be the final 12th.)

315.   No earth! A hole is empty.

316.   A very old puzzle – I am the only one going to St. Ives, it is assumed that I meet the others when they are coming towards me (away from St. Ives).

317.   729, this may not be the answer you expected, to keep the shape a cube, when we remove a top layer, we need to remove sides as well. (If you interpret the question as needing to remove a layer from top and bottom and sides, we would only have 512 cubes left).

318.   5 minutes

319.   Well, in this case, the # symbol seems to represent multiple operations, first subtraction, then addition, then multiplication so 7#6 would be = 11342

320.   19

321.   There are four times as many red ping pong balls as green, so the number of red balls can be represented as "4x". There are also six more blue balls than green balls, so the number of blue balls can be represented as "x + 6". We know that the total number of balls in the bag is 60, so we can set up an equation: x + 4x + (x + 6) = 60. Simplifying the equation, we get: 6x + 6 = 60. Subtracting 6 from both sides, we get: 6x = 54. Dividing both sides by 6, we get: x = 9. So there are 9 green balls, 4 times as many red balls (36), and 6

more blue balls than green (15). Therefore, there are 9 green balls, 36 red balls, and 15 blue balls in the bag.

322.   50%; only 70 people are required for a 99.9% chance.

323.   The two cars will meet each other after one hour (40 + 60) so the bird will have been flying for one hour, so it will have flown 80 Km.

324.   One solution is: 12 – 2 (7 – 4) = 6, another solution is: 12 ÷ 2 - 7 x 4 = 6, divide 12 by 2, getting 6. Then, subtract 7 from 6, getting -1. Finally, multiply -1 by 4, getting -4. So, the equation becomes: 6 - 7 x 4 = 6; simplifying further, we get: 6 - 28 = 6. B) 12 ÷ 2 + 7 – 4 = 9

325.   Answer = 42 hours and B) 3 quarters full.

326.   21 - you might be tempted to say double that (ie 42) but person 1 shakes 6 other hands, person 2 shakes 5 hands, person 3 shakes 4 hands and so on, …. Person 6 shakes the 1 remaining hand. (6+5+4+3+2+1=21)

327.   Start both hourglasses at the same time when the 10 minute one runs out invert it and when the 12 minute one finishes (after 2 more minutes) invert it again, that will be 14 minutes.

328.   Start both hourglasses when your friend begins the test; after the 7-minute hourglass runs out, turn it over to start it again; when the 11-minute hourglass runs out 4 minutes later, turn the 7-minute hourglass again, wait for the 7-minute hourglass to run out, which lasts another 4 minutes and takes you to 15 minutes.

329.   The Bible mentions Noah with the ark, not Moses.

330.   6 men were carrying a coffin; one man was in the coffin.

331. 14 points. You spend £110 and get £22 and 11 points. Adding the £8 to the £22 gives you £30. You spend £30 and get £6 and 3 points, so altogether you have 11 + 3 = 14 points (plus £6).

332. By putting a second consecutive bullet in a chamber, the chances are 3 in 6. As chamber 1 did not fire we now have a 1 in 4 chance but if we spin, it will be 1 in 3 so, with 2 consecutive bullets, it is worth re-spinning the chamber.

333. Less

334. This is, as it were, bad maths or faulty accounting; the bet cost them £25, they gave £2 away and split the last £3 between them.

335. The number 8

336. Put the of coins in a row and number them 1 to 10. Then take one coin out of the first bag, two out of the second, three out of the third and so on. Now put all of these coins on the scale. If these were all fake coins, they would weigh exactly 55 ounces. If the pile weighs 0.01 ounces more than that, you know that is one real coin so the real gold must be in bag 1. If it is in bag 2 it will be 55.02 ounces and so on.

337. The next in the sequence is 8: = the number of letters each month has – the word December has 8 letters.

338. The other 5 spaces are numbered: 16 06 68 88 – 98. What is the number that is covered by the car? We are looking at these numbers upside down – if we were standing in the car park (in front of these spaces) we would read 86, 87, 88, 89, 90 and 91. The missing number (covered by the parked car) is 87.

339.   Just 1 day quicker. After the first day, the 1 square meter would have doubled to 2 anyway.

340.   21 times

341.   Answer = move the minus sign above the second 10 (thus 10 T0 10 = 9:50) i.e., Ten to Ten

342.   Answer = your number is 5. You know that 2 numbers add up to the 3rd so you must be either 1 (2 + 1 = 3) or 5 (2 + 3 = 5). If it is 1 then Leon would see 1 and 3 and would think their number could be 2 or 4. Kevin would see 1 on your head and 2 on Leon's and assume he must be 1 or 3. But we know that all the numbers are different so Kevin's cannot be 1 but did not figure that out so you must be 5. If you are 5 Leon will see that and Kevin's 3 and will not know he is 2 or 8. Kevin will see your 5 and Leon's 2 and not know if he is 3 or 7. Their confusion confirms your guess.

343.   When the time is 3:15, the hour hand would be pointing due East at the 3 on the clock face and the minute hand would be pointing slightly below the 3 because it is on its way towards the next hour = 4. The minute hand should be 25% of the way from 3 o'clock. The angle between the two hands would be 7.5 degrees. 360 degrees in a circle represent 12 hours so = 30 degrees per hour. 25% of 30 = 7.5

344.   7. Explanation - 7 wearing socks minus 4 wearing both = 3, 5 wearing shoes minus 4 wearing both = 1, so 3 only socks plus 1 only shoes plus 4 both = 8, 15 minus 8 = 7.

345.   Answer = they have played 11 holes. David lost 3 bets but has won 8 holes and is £50 up, 5 + 3 + 3 = 11.

346.   7 is the most common roll with two six-sided dice. You are six times more likely to roll a 7 than a 2 or a 12, twice as

likely to roll a 7 as a 4 or a 10 and only 1.2 times more likely to roll a 7 than a 6 or an 8.

347.   Use some of the money to buy one more gold coin then give the wife 9 coins, the son 6 coins and the nephew 3 coins and divide what is left of the money in a similar way.

348.   Chicago.

349.   65292

350.   40, the song mentions 5 gold rings that start on the 5th day and continue to the 12th day so it repeats for 8 days, 5 times 8 = 40 gold rings.

BRAINTEASERS

351.   This is a good one: O,T,T,F,F,S,S, **E, N, T** (Eight, Nine, Ten)

352.   The yacht will rise with the tide so the same number of rungs will be showing in 4 hours' time.

353.   When is L bigger than XL? When you are using Roman numerals: L = 50, X = 10, XL = 40.

354.   Still 50 : 50

355.   Anyone living should not be buried!

356.   Bungalows are single-story buildings – they do not have stairs.

357.   The sixth person takes the egg and the basket.

358.   C and Y

359.   It is a coconut tree (not a banana)

360.   The multi-story car park was very busy and they had to drive round and round the circular ramps to get up to the top floor before they found a space.

361.   The restaurant was in a zoo and Derek was a large python that had escaped.

362.   You could make a T shape by placing the end of one fuse so that it touches the middle of the other, then light the bottom end of the T the first-string fuse will burn for 30

minutes, then it will light the second which burns left and right for 15 minutes each.

363.   Before Mount Everest was discovered, it was still the highest mountain on Earth.

364.   A sundial and an hourglass.

365.   No, the earl is a baby in a pushchair, collected by his mother.

366.   He is a graffiti artist and someone knocked down the wall he was working on.

367.   Holes

368.   They were musicians hired to play for a wedding.

369.   You put one yellow marble in one bucket and the rest of the marbles into the other bucket. By doing this, you increase the probability from 50% to about 75%.

370.   They all end in the name of a country except parishioner.

371.   She was counting her knitting and lost track.

372.   Question a) who will figure it out? Question b) Alan gives the correct answer; how did he work it out? Explanation: If Alan and Susan both have NO stickers, Julia would be able to see them and guess she must have a YES. If Alan has a NO, Susan would be able to work out her own sticker when Julia remained silent. But since Susan can see a YES, she cannot be certain. Alan realizes that, since both Julia and Susan are uncertain, he must have a YES sticker.

373.   The word Wholesome

374.   Neither of them had belly buttons, so no umbilical cord.

375. The 4 glasses problem. Turn 1: Choose a pair of glasses that are diagonally opposite and turn both glasses up. Turn 2: Choose a pair of adjacent glasses; at least one of the glasses will be up because of the previous step. If the other is down, then turn that glass up as well; if the barman has not spoken, there are now three glasses up and one down. Turn 3: Choose a pair of glasses that are diagonally opposite. If one is down, then turn it up and the barman will speak. If both the glasses are up, then turn one down. There are now two glasses in down position and they must be adjacent. Turn 4: Choose a pair of adjacent glasses and reverse both glasses. If both the glasses were in the same position then the barman will speak; otherwise, there are now two glasses down and they must be diagonally opposite. Turn 5: Choose a pair of glasses that are diagonally opposite and reverse both the glasses. Now, all the glasses are in the same position either up or down and the barman will tell you that you have completed the task.

376. Portia, like a true lawyer, points out that the contract only mentions flesh, no blood can be taken. She also makes one of Shakespeare's most famous speeches that starts: "The quality of mercy is not strained; It droppeth as the gentle rain from heaven, Upon the place beneath. It is twice blest; It blesseth him that gives and him that takes:"

377. She worried that he did have a live mouse in his pocket and whatever she guessed, he would deliberately prove her wrong. If she said it was dead, he would bring it out alive; if she guessed it was alive, he would kill it.

378. Question Mark. (a simple effective message =?)

379. Answer = "*My wish is that my mother can see her grandson swinging on a swing of gold in the garden of the family mansion.*"

183

380.   She suggested that he remove one wheel nut from each of the other three wheels and use them to fasten the 4th wheel back on. That would allow him to get to a garage or spares / repair shop.

381.   He should buy some padding and a cardboard box that is 4 foot long by 3 foot wide and he will be able to fit a 5-foot rod into that, corner to corner = (a 3 x 4 x 5 triangle).

382.   Answer = you input the number of the first runner to cross the line to the calculator, then add the next runner's number to that, then the third number, and so on. If all the runners come home, your total score will be 3,240. If one runner is missing that number will be deducted from the total.

383.   They are all 3 letter airport codes.

384.   The coffee still had sugar in it.

385.   D. The letters represent the notes in the diatonic musical scale: Do, Re, Mi, Fa, Sol, La, Ti, Do.

386.   Separate the 12 balls into 3 groups. Weigh group 1 and 2 against each other by placing 4 balls in each tray – if one group is heavier then remove the light group and take two of the balls from the heavy group, put them in the other tray and see which tray is heavier, then take 1 from the heavy side and do the same again. If groups 1 and 2 weigh the same, divide the 4 balls in group 3 into two and put 2 balls in each tray then follow the process as above.

387.   It is a Rock paper scissors knockout.

388.   Either fill the hole with water so that the ball floats to the surface or use a vacuum cleaner to suck it out.

389.   When the trains meet, they must be equally close (or far away) from the coast.

390.   The F1 driver saw the spectators all suddenly standing up, horrified, staring at something around the corner in front of him.

391.   2 teachers and 1 child cross, 1 teacher rows back, then 1 teacher and 1 child cross and 1 teacher returns, then 2 teachers and 1 child cross, and all 6 are on the other side.

392.   Use the "I cut, you choose" approach, say that one child can divide the ice cream and fill the bowls and the other can choose which bowl they want.

393.   The ICAO phonetic alphabet has assigned 26 code words to the 26 letters of the English alphabet in alphabetical order. The names of the girl, the sport, the country, the province, the award and the baseball team are: Juliet, Golf, India, Oscar, Quebec, and Yankee.

394.   You are standing on an ancient pyramid, one person at each corner and one on the tip.

395.   A watermelon, eat the flesh, drink the juice, plant the seeds and give the pig the rinds.

396.   Phone or text your daughter and tell her to buy a small padlock. Send the jewellery box to her with your padlock locked on it and tell her to add her padlock then send it back to you. You will then unlock your padlock and send the jewelry box back to her. She will undo her padlock and open the box.

397.   The virus will take 57 days (it doubles every day, 60 = 8/8, 59 = 4/8, 58 = 2/8 and 57 = 1/8th).

398. The 4 people were: a brother, a sister, the brother's son, the sister's daughter; the brother is a father and uncle, the sister is a mother and aunt, the son is a cousin and a nephew, the daughter is a cousin and a niece.

399. A B G D E Z E _ Answer = T for Theta, these are the first letters in the Greek alphabet, Alpha, Beta, Gamma, Delta, Epsilon, Zeta, Eta, and Theta.

400. The teacher told them to put their right hand up if they knew the answer and put their left hand up if they did not know the answer.

Amusing

401.　Whatever you went to find! Because once you find it, you stop looking.

402.　Concrete floors are very hard to crack.

403.　Time to fix the fence.

404.　There was a snowman on the lawn (with a hat, a carrot for a nose, a scarf and black coat buttons) but the snow melted.

405.　The man looks in the mirror, sees what he saw, takes the saw, cuts the table in half, puts the two halves together to make a whole and climbs out through the hole.

406.　A jeweler sells watches and a jailer watch cells.

407.　An umbrella.

408.　Meat.

409.　A garbage truck.

410.　Their middle names.

411.　Kangaroos – their tails get in the way.

412.　42.

413.　Your legs

414.　Otto Titzling (aka Titslinger) is a fictional character created by humorist Wallace Reyburn as the inventor of the bra in the 1971 book "Bust-Up: The Uplifting Tale of Otto Titzling", published by Macdonald in London and by

Prentice-Hall in the USA. He did not invent the bra. Thomas Crapper is a different story; he was real. Crapper worked for years as a plumber but did not invent the flushable toilet. That is credited to Edward Jennings. Crapper did however make many improvements to the toilet, including one that is still used today - the ballcock.

415.   EDAM (= the word "made" backwards)

416.   Bert is a cat.

417.   Noise (amongst other things like: chaos, a scene, commotion, ….)

418.   An apple a day keeps the doctor away!

419.   A leek.

420.   Land a flying saucer.

421.   A shoe!

422.   He is a thief and he got a fright when the parrot in the room he entered shouted: "*hands up*".

423.   Americans open the fridge over 20 times a day, on average.

424.   The baby, because she is a little Bigger.

425.   Use a pencil.

426.   She got bored waiting and left!

427.   To avoid disturbing mythical communities of elves that live there.

428.   BEFORE the game starts, the score is 0 – 0!

429.   Add a G and it is G one.

430.   £4. Starting with £2 for a chicken gives £4 for a duck which in the equation of 3C + 1D = 2G means that 3*2 + 1*4 = 2*Goose= 10. So, a goose = £5. Putting those values into the other equation 3G + 1C + 2D = £25. So, a duck is £4.

DETECTIVE STORIES

431.   The police arrested him because they had not told him where the scene of the crime was.

432.   The judge noticed that the accused man, Brian, was the only person who did not look up at the doors to see his wife come into the courtroom. Brian knew she was not going to appear because he had killed her.

433.   The man in black clothes was a hired assassin. The old man lived alone and was suffering, in great pain, from a long illness that was not going to get better. He did not want to commit suicide, so he paid someone else to do it for him and make it look like a break-in.

434.   If the police just pressed the PLAY button, the tape had been wound back to the start – before the gunshot – a suicide could not have done that.

435.   The backpack was a parachute that did not open.

436.   The husband waited until he thought his wife was asleep then turned off the gas at the mains, waited a minute or two and switched it on again – flooding the room with gas. He turned the gas off again before the fire brigade arrived – this was his mistake.

437.   The Math's teacher – no students in school yet so what exam papers?

438.   She pressed the gun against her husband's toes to leave prints – she knew that by the time anyone thought of that possibility, the man would have been cremated or buried.

439.   This escape would have taken careful planning and precise timing. The prisoner must walk about halfway down the path towards the exit but then (before the guards make their regular check) turn around and walk back towards the prison – they present themselves at the gate and ask to see one of the prisoners. The guards will have seen a person going along the path in the direction of the prison and will ask if they have written permission from the governor to enter. The prisoner, of course, says no, so the guards send the prisoner back the way they came towards the exit and watch as that clever ex-prisoner leaves.

440.   A person jumping from a balcony to commit suicide could not lock the balcony door from the inside.

441.   The other people in the room are all female.

442.   It is impossible to believe that the husband had time to explain that long complicated dream if he died of shock immediately, he woke up.

443.   The poison was in the ice and the ice took a while to melt so the early departing visitor left before the poison melted into the fruity punch drink.

444.   How did he know which brother had been murdered?

445.   The man was a paraglider or parachutist.

446.   His present was a boomerang.

447.   Robert was working undercover; he had been put in prison, in the same cell as Jack Stone, to gain his confidence, exchange secrets and extract a confession.

448. The widow was looking through the dining room bay windows from the garden and saw the butler hit the cook.

449. The man stood on a large block of ice.

450. The travel agent had wondered at the time when the politician ordered two air flight tickets for him and his wife because one was a return ticket and the other was one-way.

REAL WORLD

451. Unable to carry the whole moose back, some hunters cut the head and antlers off as a trophy and carry that through the woods. Unfortunately, on more than one occasion, another hunter, seeing this animal on the move, has assumed it is a live moose and shot it. Because of this trigger-happy phenomenon, some farmers have taken to writing the word COW in large letters on the sides of their cattle to try to avoid any confusion problems.

452. A cricket pitch is 22 yards long (66 feet, which is called a chain), and an acre is 22 yards wide (a chain by a 220-yard furlong).

453. They spent £16,000 on umbrellas to shelter those queuing in the rain.

454. A change in the law in Italy resulted in a sudden run of sales of white T-shirts with a black diagonal stripe – why? In order to avoid wearing a seat belt, or if their car did not have seat belts, some Italian drivers wore a Tee shirt with a black diagonal strip to pretend they were wearing a seat belt.

455. Construction workers had nicknamed the bridge Galloping Gertie because, in windy conditions, the roadway moved vertically and buckled. The bridge's main span collapsed in 40-mile-per-hour winds on the morning of November 7, 1940, as the deck oscillated in an alternating twisting motion that gradually increased in amplitude until it

tore apart. Scientists, engineers, and bridge builders learnt important lessons from this disaster.

456.　He was a keen golfer and wanted to get a hole in one. He had promised that, if he did achieve this ambition, he would buy everyone in the club a drink.

457.　A square manhole cover can be turned and dropped down the diagonal of the manhole. A round manhole cover cannot be dropped down the manhole, so all manhole covers should be round.

458.　The first Popeye comic strip series appeared in 1931. Popeye was famously strong and he ate lots of spinach. Kids and many adults presumed they could build muscles by consuming lots of this green vegetable.

459.　Rather incredibly, Johann Hurlinger walked on his hands for 1,400 km from Vienna in Austria to Paris in France in 55 daily 10-hour stints averaging 2.54 km/h.

460.　Burp or belch! As loudly and extravagantly as possible.

461.　It was nicknamed the "Empty State Building" for years because while it was built in the great depression so it was cheap to build (plenty of people looking for work and wages were low), but few businesses had enough money to pay the rental rates. It did not turn a profit until 1947.

462.　The Milgram experiment would not be allowed today, it would not gain ethical approval. Stanley Milgram, a psychologist at Yale University, wanted to investigate the conflict between obedience to authority and personal conscience. He examined justifications for acts of genocide offered by those accused at the World War II, Nuremberg War Criminal trials. Their defense said they were just following orders from their superiors. In this research, people (volunteers) were told they were testing if punishment would make others learn but actually the experiment was set up to test how far people would go when told to do something. – would they obey someone apparently in authority or rebel and refuse to keep giving some other person increasingly powerful electric shocks, despite hearing screams and pleadings from the actors engaged to play the part of those being "educated". The astonishing findings were that 65% of these participants did keep going through the process, believing they were administering punishments, right up to the limit on the dial (apparently 450 volts) labelled XXX! (indicating a potentially fatal amount). All of the participants kept going until 300 volts, which was labelled DANGER!

463.   The Greeks said they were afraid of the long voyage home so they had left the big wooden horse as a gift for the sea god. Despite warnings, the Trojans took the 'gift" inside the city gates as a victory trophy, believing the Greeks had gone home. That night Greek warriors emerged from it, killed the guards and opened the gates to let the returned Greek army in. The story is told in the Aeneid and is mentioned in the Odyssey.

464.   This is an early example of spin, real estate exaggeration / lies. The Saga of Erik the Red states: "In the summer, Erik left to settle in the country he had found, which he called Greenland, as he said people would be attracted there if it had a favorable name."

465.   Rather incredibly, the pieces did not fit together; the designers had used different CAD programs which resulted in different measurements.

466. These dogs had been trained to take bombs that were strapped on their backs, under enemy tanks and armored vehicles. There was a lever above the bomb that set it off as the dog ducked under. If any dog did not carry out this mission and instead began to return towards the soldiers, they shot it, in case the bomb went off when it got back.

467. One of the most important jobs of a golf club pro in giving lessons. Most players are right-handed. It is suggested that it is easier to learn from left-handed golf coaches because they face their clients when they stand in front of them.

468. The archers were showing (in an exaggerated, aggressive and dramatic way) that the fingers they used to pull the bow string and arrow back were still intact because it was the custom to cut these fingers off prisoners of war to prevent them using a bow.

469. Scotland allows three different verdicts in court, guilty, not guilty and not proven. Not guilty and not proven are both acquittals. The (inventive) lawyer argued that the man had always wanted to buy a gorgeous fur coat for his wife's birthday but always felt too embarrassed and "working class" to enter a fancy furrier shop. Instead, the man had decided that the best plan would be to borrow 6 fur coats and take them back to his wife to let her try them on in the comfort and less stressful surroundings of her home. He could then find out which one she liked best, take the rest back to the shop in the morning and pay for the one he had kept. The verdict was "not proven".

470. Aerial photographs provided detailed and accurate maps that allowed the government to assess property and land values more precisely, which led to more accurate taxation and ensured that property owners and landholders paid their

fair share of taxes, thus increasing government revenue. Images of the landscape from above enabled the government to identify and map valuable resources like minerals and potential agricultural lands, which could then be utilized or leased to generate revenue. Aerial photographs provided a better understanding of the terrain, existing infrastructure, and potential areas for development so the government could plan urban expansion and projects, leading to increased economic activity and higher tax revenues from the newly developed areas. Detailed aerial images helped them to manage natural resources more effectively and sustainably, including: forestry, water, wildlife and conservation areas. Aerial photographs also had military applications, the government could plan defense strategies which could contribute to economic stability and growth. Finally, the government could identify areas in need of development, such as roads, bridges, and transportation networks. Investing in infrastructure spurred economic growth, attracted businesses and tourists, and increased tax revenue through increased economic activity.

471. Ignaz Semmelweis's discovery was a ground-breaking contribution to the field of medicine and is now recognized as a crucial milestone in the history of medical hygiene. He observed that the mortality rate from childbed fever was considerably higher in the clinic where medical students and doctors conducted deliveries compared to the clinic where midwives delivered babies. After years of meticulous research and analysis, Semmelweis worked out that the higher mortality rate in the doctors' clinic was associated with the fact that doctors were in the habit of performing autopsies on deceased patients and then proceeding directly to examine pregnant women without handwashing. At that time, the

concept of germs and infection transmission was not understood. He implemented a strict handwashing policy using a chlorine solution for the doctors before attending to patients in the delivery room and this reduced the incidence of childbed fever in the doctors' clinic dramatically. Semmelweis published his findings and urged other medical institutions to adopt similar hygiene practices. However, his ideas faced resistance and scepticism from the medical community of the time, and he was met with significant opposition. It took several years and the work of later scientists like Louis Pasteur and Joseph Lister to solidify the germ theory of disease and promote the importance of hygiene in medical practice.

472.   Introduced in Britain on May 6, 1840, the Penny Black stamp was the world's first adhesive postage stamp. It featured a profile of Queen Victoria and had a face value of one penny, allowing prepayment of postage for letters up to half an ounce in weight within the UK. The Penny Black was revolutionary and played a crucial role in the development of modern postal systems. however, it was replaced by the Penny Red after only one year due to several practical reasons. The design posed a problem with the cancellation of stamps because it was difficult to see any cancellation marks, (which were meant to prevent stamps from being reused). People could not only wash the ink off the Penny Black and reuse it they could also forge or counterfeit it. The Penny Red was introduced on February 10, 1841, as a replacement for the Penny Black. It featured a similar design but with a significant difference, the color was changed from black to red which made it easier to apply and read cancellation marks and reduced reuse and forgery.

473.   "The Ghost Army" was a unique and highly classified unit of the United States Army during World War II. Officially known as the 23rd Headquarters Special Troops, it was a special unit formed to mislead and deceive the enemy by creating illusions and spreading disinformation. The Ghost Army was made up of artists, designers, engineers, actors, and other creative individuals who used their skills to design and execute these deception operations. They set out to impersonate large, formidable Allied military units, diverting the attention of enemy forces away from the actual locations and movements of Allied troops. They created inflatable rubber tanks, trucks, and artillery pieces to deceive enemy reconnaissance. They used sophisticated sound systems to produce fake noises of military activity, such as vehicle and troop movements, guns and radio communications, reinforcing the illusion of large forces. They set up fake signs and signals and spread false information through captured German soldiers or radio broadcasts, leading the Germans to believe in the presence of non-existent units. The reason "The Ghost Army" was kept a secret for nearly 50 years was to preserve its effectiveness as a military deception tactic. Information about the Ghost Army was classified, and the unit's activities remained largely unknown to the public until the late 1990s. Today, "The Ghost Army" is recognized as an extraordinary example of ingenuity, creativity and lateral thinking.

474.   Someone forgot to check that the gun was not loaded and an actor fired it at her.

475.   Altruism, the man was a retired leprosy doctor; he knew how vital a healthy kidney was to someone in need and decided he could give one away.

476. The person who painted the boiled egg is a professional clown. Every clown creates and, as it were, a trademark, a unique look. A lot depends on the face. They claim the image on the egg as theirs and that is deposited at the international clown's club egg registry. Clowns International has been painting the faces of its members on eggs for over 70 years. Each one is a record of a clown's unique identity, preserving the unwritten rule that no clown should copy another's look.

477. The staff at the hospital dressed the teddy bears and cuddly toys up with bandages and explained to the children / patients that the poor things needed to stay in hospital for treatment and to get better. The children were sympathetic and understood.

478. Answer = poor estimation and planning. The cost of attempting to register the estimated 15 million guns owned by Canada's 34 million residents quickly climbed past $600 million and staffing for the new system rose to 600 employees. In 2002, Canada's auditor general released a report saying initial cost estimates of $2 million (Canadian) had increased to $1 billion. Police estimated that only 2-16% of guns used in crimes were stolen from legal owners and thus potentially in the registry. The bulk of the guns were unregistered weapons imported illegally from the U.S. by criminal gangs. Finally in 2011, there was a vote to abolish the long-gun registry and destroy all.

479. You can buy bottles with a pear inside them – so this trick is possible. All you have to do is place a bottle over the tiny budding fruit when it appears and the pear will grow inside the bottle.

480. The Judgment of Solomon is a story from the Bible (the Old Testament, First book of Kings, chapter 3), that explains

how King Solomon dealt with a quarrelsome dispute between two women both claiming to be the mother of a child. After some thought, Solomon called for a sword and declared that the only fair solution was to cut the baby in two, so that each woman could be given half. This tactic revealed their true feelings and relationship to the child. One woman renounced her claim, proving that she would rather give the child up than see it killed. Solomon ordered the baby given to her, as her love was selfless, as opposed to the other woman's disregard for the baby's well-being. Some people consider this approach to justice to be an archetypal example of an impartial judge displaying wisdom in making a ruling.

481. Most cowboys in the 1800s died of diseases = dysentery, smallpox, measles, mumps, and influenza were named in diaries and journals, but consumption (tuberculosis), cholera, typhoid fever, parasites, scarlet fever and scurvy were probably the biggest killers.

482. A non-spherical egg sits on its side and this shape prevents the egg from rolling off cliffs, the egg tends to roll in a circle instead.

483. German chemist August Kekulé von Stradonitz pictured the Ouroboros, an ancient symbol depicting a serpent or dragon eating its own tail which gave him the notion of linked carbon atoms forming a benzene ring. He visualized a snake seizing its own tail, which led him to the idea of a cyclic structure for benzene.

484. Isadora Duncan died on September 14, 1927 in Nice, France. Her death was a freak and tragic accident. She was fond of flowing scarves and was strangled when the long silk scarf she was wearing got entangled in the rear wheel of the Bugatti convertible she was travelling in. She was pulled

from the car and dragged before the driver could stop. Born in San Francisco in 1877 she moved to Europe to become a dancer when she was in her early 20s.

485.   King George IV is famous for having a right shoe and a left shoe. Until that time, most shoes or boots were made to be worn on either foot unless you were rich enough to have a pair specially made. Actually, it is probably a bit of a coincidence that left and right shoes started to appear about that time – he may not have been such a trendsetter – they became more affordable.

486.   When Alexander Fleming returned from a holiday, he removed the tops from some old petri dishes and noticed that the bacteria he had grown were being killed by a mould. The mould produced a substance that killed many disease-causing bacteria. He identified the mould as being from the Penicillium genus, and, after some months of calling it "mould juice", named the substance it released penicillin on 7 March 1929. This discovery was a major medical breakthrough, his discovery started the antibiotic revolution and sealed his lasting reputation. He was recognized for that achievement in 1945, when he received the Nobel Prize for Physiology or Medicine, along with Howard Walter Florey and Ernst Boris Chain, who isolated and purified penicillin.

487.   The Boston, Massachusetts, Cocoanut Grove nightclub fire, that took place in on November 28, 1942, resulted in the deaths of 492 people. It is the deadliest nightclub fire in U.S. history and the second-deadliest single-building fire. Fire regulations had been flouted: some exit doors had been locked to prevent unauthorized entry, and the elaborate palm tree décor contained flammable materials. The air-conditioning used flammable gas because of the wartime

shortage of freon. Following the fire, many new laws were enacted for public establishments, including the banning of flammable decorations, a provision that emergency exits must be kept unlocked (from the inside), and that revolving doors cannot be the only exit.

488.   Post-It Notes were invented by accident. Art Fry was aware of Silver's reusable adhesive, he also sang in a church choir and had a regular problem of losing his hymn notes in his church song book so he suggested using the adhesive on the backs of paper so that they could be stuck and removed without leaving residue.

489.   The reason that women's buttons are on the left side, while men's are on the right goes back a long way. When buttons were invented in the 13th century, they were very expensive. Wealthy women did not dress themselves, their maid did. Since most people were right-handed, it was easier for someone standing in front of the lady to do her buttons up. Nowadays it is just tradition.

490.   Cooper asked for 4 parachutes to avoid the possibility that the authorities might consider giving him a dud or improper parachute. Asking for 4 parachutes implied he might take some passengers or crew with him; authorities could not be sure.

491.   Vulfpeck released Sleepify in March 2014 as a means to fund a concert tour of the same name; all of the shows were to be free of charge but funded solely using royalty payments from the album on the music streaming service Spotify.

492.   Abraham Wald, and the Statistical Research Group which Wald was a part of, examined the damage done to aircraft that had returned from missions and recommended adding

armor to the areas that showed the least damage because these were the planes that managed to return (survivorship bias) and it was more important to reinforce the parts that caused more critical harm. Bullet holes in returning aircraft must be in areas where a bomber could take damage and still fly well enough to return safely to base. So, Wald inferred that planes hit in other areas were the ones most likely to be lost.

493.   Publishers of atlases and dictionaries protect their work from copyright infringers by putting non-existent places, islands and words in their publications so that it is easy to see if anyone has copied them and display clear evidence if they have.

494.   The clever kidnapper had placed a small bird cage, with two pigeons in it, in the phone booth. Instructions attached to the cage told the father to put the 10 diamonds into the little bags tied to the homing pigeon's legs and let them go. The birds flew off untraceably.

495.   Following Great Britain's adoption of the Gregorian calendar in 1752, George Washington's birthday shifted one year and eleven days to February 22, 1732.

496.   Jenner's work represented the first scientific attempt to control an infectious disease by the deliberate use of vaccination. He had heard that dairymaids were protected from smallpox naturally after having suffered from cowpox. In May 1796, Jenner found a dairymaid named Sarah Nelms who had fresh cowpox lesions. He inoculated an 8-year-old boy, James Phipps, using matter from her lesions. The boy developed mild fever and discomfort, but after 10 days was much better. Jenner inoculated the boy again in July. No disease developed, and Jenner concluded that protection was

complete. The Latin word for cow is Vacca, and cowpox is Vaccinia; Jenner decided to call this new procedure vaccination.

497.   About 2%. The biomass of wild mammals on land and at sea is dwarfed by the combined weight of cattle, pigs, sheep and other domesticated mammals. The biomass of livestock has reached about 651 million tons = 27 times the weight of all wild terrestrial mammals (24 million tons) and 15 times that of wild marine mammals (40 million tons). The biomass of humans amounts to another 394 million tons.

498.   Aeschylus returned to Sicily, where he died in 456 or 455 BC. Valerius Maximus wrote that he was killed by a tortoise dropped by an eagle which had mistaken his head for a rock suitable for shattering the shell. Pliny wrote that Aeschylus had been staying outdoors to avoid a prophecy that he would be killed by a falling object.

499.   Archduke Franz Ferdinand was wearing a military uniform that included a tight-fitting tunic with intricate buttons and clasps. Uniforms of that era were often tailored to be form-fitting and stylish and it is said that he was so vain that he was sewn into his clothing, making it far more challenging to remove quickly. Gavrilo Princip shot the Archduke and his wife, Sophie, while they were in an open-top car during a motorcade. The archduke's attendants could not undo his coat swiftly enough to stop the bleeding. The assassination was a significant event that ultimately triggered a chain of events leading to the outbreak of World War I. The political tensions and alliances in Europe at the time turned the assassination into a catalyst for an unprecedented global conflict.

500.　Spielberg reduced the number of scenes that the shark appears in and instead hinted and inferred its presence more. He built tension and fear in the imagination of the audience and used an innovative and evocative musical theme, written by John Williams, to increase the drama, thrills and anticipation. Cinema goers were far more frightened of what was below the surface because they could not see it, most of the time. Critics and audiences raved about the film and it probably kick-started Spielberg's rise to fame.

501.　The man was Pablo Picasso and the builder knew that Picasso's drawings alone would be worth far more than he would normally make from building an extension.

502.　It was said to have been painted after he had been beheaded; the legend suggests that his head was sewn back onto his body in order to produce the painting. It is said that the executioner took at least 5 blows to sever the head. Another rumor says that he was the man in the iron mask.

503.　It was regarded by some as just a cynical, clever advertising stunt. When the bronze sculpture known as 'Fearless Girl', designed by Kristen Visbal, was erected in the Financial District of Manhattan, looking at the well-known 'Charging Bull' statue, it was hailed by some as a recognition and glorification of the strength and resilience of women. The young girl staring down a raging bull - an emblem of masculine virility – was said to be symbolic and the fact that it stands in New York City's male-dominant financial district was impressive. Others regard it far more cynically as fake feminism and a blatant advertising ploy used to gain favor and hide the ugliness of financial dealing. The US government had been scrutinizing State Street's compensation and discrimination practices. "Fearless Girl" came along while the company was worried about reputational harm.

504.   The reason was that they were more likely to die if they were hit with shrapnel when they wore cloth caps. Wearing metal helmets did protect them a bit but while fewer men died of fatal shrapnel head wounds, more of them sustained injuries that did not kill them. The relative number of head injuries increased compared to the number of deaths.

505.   James B. Hargis and his mechanic, Charles Creighton, drove in reverse from New York to Los Angeles and back again (almost 7,200 miles). Apart from a 48-hour rest in LA, they traveled night and day at an average speed of 10 mph. Over 50 years later, Brian "Cub" Keene and James "Wilbur" Wright reversed their Chevrolet Blazer over 9,000 miles, passing through 15 US states and parts of Canada from 1st August to 6th September 1984.

506.   Bury the bodies vertically.

507.   Trot is 2 beat, canter is 3 beat and gallop is 4 beat.

508.   The Sydney Opera House project was about 15 times over budget and 10 years late yet has become one of Australia's most famous icons. Begun in 1957, the estimated opening date was January 1963 but because it was such a complex and innovative project, it was not finished until 1973. The original budget was $7m but the final bill was $102m, a 1,457% increase.

509.   The Stanford Prison experiment went wrong very quickly with harsh and strangely unsympathetic psychological abuse of the prisoners by the "guards" which became increasingly brutal; it had to be ended on the sixth day. The experiment appeared to show how quickly someone or a group, given

authority over others, abuse that power and inflict control, unwarranted punishment, and fear. This experiment has been referenced and critiqued as one of the most unethical psychology experiments in history. The harm inflicted on the participants prompted universities worldwide to improve their ethics requirements for human subjects of experiments. Other researchers have found it difficult to reproduce the study, and some critics have described the study as unscientific and fraudulent.

510.   Ludger Sylbaris was one of the survivors in the city of Saint-Pierre on the Caribbean Island of Martinique during the volcanic eruption of Mount Pelée on May 8, 1902. The city was in the direct path of a huge pyroclastic flow, which destroyed it in less than a minute and killed an estimated 30,000 people. The underground jail cell protected him sufficiently although he did receive burns. Sylbaris later traveled with the Barnum & Bailey circus, became a celebrity, and was known as "the man who lived through Doomsday".

ELIMINATION

511.   Anne = trampolining, Jeremy = canoeing, Marie = rock climbing, Bob = orienteering.

512.   Three.

513.   Alison is allergic to shellfish, Bruce to bee stings, Charlie to nuts, Fred to pollen, and Sarah to cats.

514.   You figure out that 79 are liars and 1 is honest. One of them is honest so the first piece of information is satisfied. If you take the honest man and any other politician, the other politician must be a liar to satisfy the second piece of information, "If you take any two politicians, at least one of them is a liar." So, 79 are liars.

515.   The students should order all the rounds at once on three trays. Tray 1 – ask for two Ouzos, a Cointreau, a Kahlua and a Port (now they know the Ouzo).   On Tray 2 – they ask for two Advocaats, a Crème de Menthe, a Calvados and a Port. (Now they know the Advocaat and Port) On Tray 3 – ask for two Parfait d'amours, a Sloe Gin, a Calvados and a Kahlua (now they know what the Parfait d'amour, Crème de Menthe, Cointreau, Sloe Gin, Calvados and Kahlua are).

Another way that the students could approach this problem, and get all the drinks for free, is to try to identify the drinks based on their taste, color, and any other distinguishing characteristics. They could use their phones / Google to look up these characteristics, team up and compare their observations to help them derive the names of the drinks.

For example, Cointreau is a liqueur with an orange flavor and aroma; Ouzo is an anise-flavored aperitif which becomes cloudy white when mixed with water; Parfait d'amour is a purple or lilac colored curaçao-based liqueur flavored with rose petals, vanilla pods and almonds; Crème de Menthe is a green, mint-flavored liqueur; Calvados is an apple brandy; Port is a sweet, fortified, deep-red wine; Advocaat is a creamy, yellow colored liqueur made from eggs, sugar, and brandy; Sloe Gin is a red liqueur made from gin and sloe berries; and Kahula is a dark-brown, coffee-flavored liqueur. They can taste each drink and take notes on their unique characteristics.

516.   You suspect that the barman dunnit. At first, he said he tripped over the old man in the dark then he said he noticed the body, sounds like one statement is a lie.

517.   Mary wore a yellow dress and a ring. Anne wore a blue dress and earrings. Jennifer wore a black dress and a bracelet. Lucy wore a red dress and a necklace.

518.   This is a really good puzzle. Answer = Take the first 13 cards off the top of the deck and flip them over. Leave the other pile of 39 cards alone. You have done it! If that solution seems too simple, lets take an example – suppose there happen to be 8 face up cards in your pile of 13, that leaves 5 face ups in the other pile. When you turn over your pile of 13 you overturn the 8 and now 5 are face up, so both piles have equal amounts of face up cards! Try it yourself with a different number.

519.   Answer = the killer was the mother, victim was the son. We know that the youngest was not the victim (f) or the helper (g) or the killer (e). So the youngest must be the witness. Father is oldest, mother next oldest, daughter is youngest. There are 3 possible scenarios: 1) The father is the

helper, the mother the victim and the son the murderer 2) the father the helper the mother the murderer, the son the victim and 3) the father is the murderer, the mother is the helper and the son is the victim. A process of elimination shows it must be option 2, (victim and youngest were of different sexes, helper and witness were of different sexes.)

520.   Answer = Yes, if Jeff is an agent spying on Caroline, the statement is true. If Jeff is a traitor, then Tim (who is an agent) is spying on a traitor – so, once again, the statement is true.

521.   Choose the bat exit – vampire bats sleep during the day, only come out at night and don't usually eat humans. If they did drink your blood, they would only consume about 1 ounce (2 tablespoons) of it.

522.   Kenny is Samantha's father, Arthur is Eric' father and Micky is John's father.

523.   Answer = "In which direction do you live?" The person from the community of liars will lie and direct you towards the truth-tellers and the person from the truth-telling community will also point in the direction of truthtellers.

524.   Elizabeth cannot be the nurse or the teacher, so she must be the police officer. Stanley doesn't like children so he must be the nurse.

525.   Answer = cabinet 1, the only statement that is true is on cabinet 3. If the money is in cabinet 1 then the first two statements are false and the third statement is true. If the money is in cabinet 2 then the first two statements would be true. If the money is in the third cabinet, then the first and third statements are true.

526.   From the information provided, we can deduce that the driver's name is Smith. Here's how we can figure it out:

- We know that Mr. Brown lives in Brixton, so he cannot be the passenger who lives in Tottenham.

- The conductor lives in Chelsea.

- We know that the passenger who shares the conductor's name lives in Tottenham.

- Mr Jones cannot do algebra so we can assume he is not the teacher.

- From statement 6, we know that the conductor goes to the same local pub as the passenger who is a teacher. Since local pubs are usually located near where people live, this means that the conductor and the teacher live in the same area., which is Chelsea.

- As Mr Brown lives in Brixton Mr Smith must be the teacher.

- The conductor shares a name with the passenger who lives in Tottenham – who must be Mr Jones. Therefore, the conductor is Jones.

- As Smith often beats the ticket inspector at snooker, the ticket inspector cannot be Smith (he cannot beat himself) so the ticket inspector must be Brown, this means that the driver's name must be Smith.

- So, we can conclude that the driver's name is Smith.

527.   40 socks. If you take out 38 socks (adding the two biggest amounts, 21 and 17), it is possible (though very unlikely) they could all be blue and red. To make 100 percent certain that

you have a pair of black socks, you must take out two more socks.

528.   Judy and Peter are the two liars.

529.   July 16th. This question looks difficult at first – as if it is missing some information, but we know Christine has told Joe the month of her birthday, and Bennie the day. They do not know what the other has been told. For Joe to be 'certain' that Bennie cannot know the answer - as suggested in his first statement - we can assume that the birthday is not in May or June. This is because in May and June there are numbers (dates) that only occur once across the four months - namely May 19 and June 18. If Joe had been given May or June as the month, he could not be certain that Bennie doesn't know the birthday. Bennie might have been the number 18 or 19. For Joe to be 'certain' that Bennie does not know, Joe must have been given a month that does not contain one of these 'unique' dates - i.e. July or August. Joe's disclosure now gives Bennie the clue he needs. Bennie only knows the number of Christine's birthday, but from Joe's statement he has now also ruled out both May and June. This is because he realises Albert has ruled out May and June because of the 'single number' aspect above. So there are now just five remaining dates - July 14, July 16, Aug 14, Aug 15, Aug 17 - and Bennie says he knows which is the birthday. If Christine had told Bennie that her birthday fell on the 14th of the month, then he could not have worked out the date at this stage. However, he says he now knows the date, so we can rule out July 14 and August 14. This leaves just three dates to choose from - July 16, Aug 15 and Aug 17. Following Bennie's statement, Joe is able to deduce the date of Christine's birthday. This means her birthday must be the

only remaining date in the month he was originally told. Given that there are two dates left in August and one in July, it has to be the July date. So the answer is July 16.

530.   Person 2 calls out that he must have an orange circle. Explanation: Person 1 can see 2 and 3. Person 2 can only see person 3. Person 3 cannot see anyone and neither can person 4. If 2 and 3 had the same-colored circles person 1 would see that and know (since there are only 2 of each color) that they must have the other color. So, person 1 must see two different colors in front of him. After a while, person 2 realizes he can work this out because he knows that if person 1 had seen different colors, he would have shouted out the answer. Person 2 can see that the person in front (person 3) has a green circle so knows that his own circle must be Orange.

MYSTERIES

531.   While the greying of hair is primarily influenced by genetics, lifestyle, stress, environmental factors and the aging process, some scientists have suggested that since facial hair appears years after the hair on a man's head, it has had a shorter lifespan and so appears to last longer. The greying of hair is attributed to a decrease in the production of melanin, the pigment responsible for hair color. As we age, the melanocyte cells that produce melanin gradually decrease in activity, resulting in the appearance of grey or white hair.

532.   How do these accounts make sense? Why were the 3 men in the golf club content to see the arm and why did the surgeon want to purchase a left arm? This question works best when there is a chance to ask questions. It is difficult to figure out the answer without obtaining more information and narrowing options down a bit. The answer in both cases is the same. 4 men in a small plane crash-landed, miles from anywhere, in the Andes mountains. They waited to be rescued. Days went by and no one appeared. Starving, they eventually made a solemn pact that they would consume human flesh. One of the men was a surgeon and he said he could amputate an arm from each person, which they could cook and eat. They promised that once this agreement began, all 4 men had to commit to losing an arm – whether they were rescued or not. The surgeon was the only person who still had both arms when they were eventually rescued, so,

having promised, he had to send the arm as proof once they returned to civilization.

533.   She is not tall enough to reach the 30th floor button on the wall of the lift.

534.   The police had phoned to tell him his wife had been assaulted but they did not tell him what the weapon was.

535.   Rather unbelievably, the story goes that this unfortunate man had been out for a swim in a lake when a fire-fighting aero plane had swooped down to scoop up more water to douse the nearby forest fire and scooped him up too, depositing him with the water on the fire.

536.   The poor woman had been blind all her life and was traveling, with her guide dog, to the big city hoping that the operation the hospital had offered her would allow her to see for the first time. She had the operation, stayed in the hospital for a few days to recover and was joyful to be able to see the world around her. On the way home, the train went through the dark tunnel, she had never experienced a dark tunnel before and so she thought she had lost her sight again.

537.   He jumped from the outside balcony into his room.

538.   Although the trains are getting to your station every 30 minutes, one arrives soon after the other, so, for example, the trains heading East arrive at 11:00, 11:30 and 12:00 and the trains going West arrive at 11:10, 11:40 and 12:10. So if you get to the station any time between 11:11 and 11:30, (a 19-minute window) you are going to go East. If you get there between 11:01 and 11:10 (a 9-minute window) you will catch the train to the West. In other words, it is more likely you will catch the trains heading East.

539. This is a very sad and horrifying case – the girl had been locked in a cellar all of her life and was never allowed out. All she knew about was what there was in the cellar. When she opened the door, she was suddenly able to see the rest of the house and the outside world.

540. I got off the elevator on the first floor.

541. Reports of dogs driving cars seem to stem from occasions when owners leave dogs loose in automatic cars that have been left in "park" on steep roads in San Francisco. Some dogs get anxious or boisterous and jump about inside eventually knocking the gear stick out of park. The car takes off downhill. Many of these dogs, once the car starts to roll, place their paws on the dashboard and appear to be driving as the car picks up speed, out of control.

542. They were golfers (an eagle is a score 2 below par); the other might have answered that's nothing compared to your albatross!

543. Caesar and Cleopatra are goldfish! The earth tremor made their bowl fall off the table; it hit the floor and broke, the water leaked out and the goldfish could not breathe.

544. The man was smuggling motorcycles.

545. She guessed that her husband would take the opportunity to see his lover as soon as his wife left and that he would have phoned the girlfriend to make arrangements. She pressed the redial button on the landline phone and when the woman answered, the wife told her she had won a prize draw and asked what name and address to send it to.

546. Billy was a goat; he ate the label!

547.   The police knew that Andy had quite poor eyesight and probably did not put his glasses on when he got out of bed to open the front door. It is easy to confuse 10:59 with 11:54 on an old clock when you mistake the long and short hands.

548.   Roderigo visited the sorcerer and found out what advice had been given to Cesare. Roderigo gave Cesare a glass of water and Cesare, assuming this glass was full of poison, swallowed the poisonous antidote potion that the sorcerer had given him after he had finished the glass of liquid that Roderigo had given him.

549.   Harold's message implicated JASON: 6=June; 4=April; 9=September; 10=October; 11=November.

550.   Atticus explained that there were no barbers in heaven and said that was the reason for his untidy beard. Since the Emperor now knew a way to reach his ancestors, he asked for his barber to be sent next. Realizing that he would probably die in the fire, the emperor's barber confessed what he and the 6 children had done. No one dared to conspire against Atticus again.

CRITICAL AND LATERAL

THINKING

551. The strange foreign note.

- Question f) What did he do next? Answer = he claimed he went back to the first bank and bought 10 of these notes, then cashed them in at the 4th bank, making a huge profit!

552. He said that he decided the best thing to do was to get as drunk as possible and become obnoxious. He sat in his first-class seat ordering alcoholic drinks all the way to London. By the time they landed, he could hardly walk and was talking loudly and singing; his friends had to carry him some of the way. Apparently, this trick worked – the last thing customs officials wanted to do was to stop such a drunken, noisy, obstreperous man. He went straight through customs and left the airport.

553. He guessed it might be domestic abuse. It was a cry for help. After he said this to the students, he turned back to her and tears were running down her face. He had hit the nail on the head. She had been too embarrassed to mention it in front of the young students. Call it intuition, pattern recognition or lateral thinking?

554. The older monk's reply was: "I only carried her across the river – you have been carrying her ever since".

555. Dunker's experiment: Empty the matches out of the matchbox. Take the part of the matchbox that held the matches and stick drawing pins through one of its sides into the corkboard. You now have a small platform / shelf to put the candle on. Light a match and melt the base of a candle a little bit then stick it to the matchbox shelf and light the candle. (The second candle is a spare).

556. Casu mazu contains live maggots. These maggots can jump up to five inches out of the cheese as you eat it. You are advised to protect your eyes while eating this delicacy so that the maggots cannot enter them.

557. At first sight, this puzzle might look like you need to apply some complicated formula to solve it, but once you realize (or better still draw a sketch of the problem) that, since the rope is 80 feet long and the flagpoles are 50-foot high each if you folded the rope in half, it would be two 40-foot lengths and be 10 feet from the ground so the flagpoles must be next to each other, i.e., zero feet apart.

558. Count out 20 coins, separate them from the rest and turn each of them over (flip them), once. It may seem counter-intuitive but it does not matter how many of the 20 you took were heads-up because when you turn them over, you will end up with the same number of heads-ups in both piles of coins. For example, suppose there happen to be 2 heads-up coins in the 20 you take; that means you have taken 18 that are heads down and there must be 18 heads-up coins left behind (not selected). So, when you overturn all the 20 you selected you will be turning 18 heads-down over so that they become heads-up coins. Even if you, against all odds, were to choose all 20 heads-up coins (leaving no heads-ups in the other pile), when you flip

them, you will turn all the heads down, so there will now be no heads showing.

559. Indiana University library sinks over half an inch per year because engineers failed to calculate and include the estimated weight of all the books that would be placed inside the building.

560. CABFDE. A finished before B but behind C, (so CAB). Then, we know D finished before B, (so CABD). E finished after D, and F finished after B and before D so CABFDE.

561. 10. Explanation: If only one man were cheating then his wife would work this out on the first day as she would realize that no other husbands were cheating and so the cheating husband must be hers. If there were 2 cheating husbands, then wife A would be aware that wife B's husband was cheating on her and would therefore expect that she would deduce this on the first day as in the 1 cheating husband example, because this does not happen wife A knows that wife B is also aware of a cheating husband. Since wife A was not aware of this, it must be her husband who is cheating. Wife B will go through the same thought process and so two men will be thrown out on the 2nd day. If there are 3 cheating husbands: wife C will be aware of A and B's cheating husbands and expect the process to be solved as in the 2-cheating husband example on the 2nd day when this does not happen, she will know that A and B must also be aware of 2 cheating husbands and will therefore throw her own husband out on the 3rd day. A and B will think and do the same. For N cheating husbands: Any of the wives being cheated on will be aware of N-1 cheating husbands and expect the process to be

solved on the (N-1)^th day; when this doesn't happen, they all become aware that all the other wives that they thought were being cheated were all under the same impression and hence they must be the Nth cheated on wife. Hence on the Nth day, N wives throw out N husbands. So, on the 10th day, 10 men are thrown out.

562. Looking carefully at these words reveals that all of them are animals (eel, ant, otter) with a P placed in front of them, so the only word of the 4 that fits that rule is Pox (ox).

563. Just less than 6 inches. (36 inches divided by 2 Pi = 5.76 inches.) A version of this question appears in William Whiston's The Elements of Euclid, written in 1702. Explanation = assuming that the Earth is a perfect sphere with a circumference of 40,075 kilometers (24,901 miles) at the equator, the radius can be calculated using the formula for the circumference of a circle, which is $C = 2\pi r$, where C is the circumference and r is the radius. Solving for r, we get $r = C / (2\pi)$. Plugging in the value for the circumference of the Earth, we get r = 40,075 km / (2π) ≈ 6,378 km. If we add an extra 3 feet to the length of the rope, the new circumference of the rope will be $C' = C + 3$ feet. Since 1 kilometer is about 3280.84 feet, we can convert 3 feet to kilometers: 3 feet ≈ 0.0009144 km. So, the new circumference of the rope is C' ≈ 40,075 km + 0.0009144 km ≈ 40,075.0009144 km. The new radius of the circle can be calculated using the same formula: $r' = C' / (2\pi)$. Plugging in the value for the new circumference of the rope, we get r' ≈ 40,075.0009144 km / (2π) ≈ 6,378.00014524 km. The difference between the new radius and the original radius of the Earth is approximately 6,378.00014524 km - 6,378 km ≈ 0.00014524 km. This

difference is equivalent to approximately 0.14524 meters, or about 14.5 centimeters. So, if a rope was tied tightly around a sphere the same size as the Earth's equator and an extra 3 feet was added to its length, when it was raised up uniformly as high as possible to make it tight again, it would be raised up by almost 6 inches.

564.   Cut it horizontally.

565.   If you shoot (and hit) Wyatt or Sundance, the next bullet (from either of them) will get you, so the best tactic is to shoot your first paintball up in the air (away from them). The next shooter, Sundance, must shoot Wyatt to protect himself. With Wyatt out of the way, you will have the next shot and now that there is only one person left, you can kill the remaining gunman (if you can hold your nerve and aim well).

566.   In early tests, planes flew down the beam and landed safely most of the time but if they lost the beam when close to the ground, the first program kicked back in, dropped the nose, increased power and the plane dived nose first into the runway. Corrections were made quicky but a new problem emerged – the aircraft landed on exactly the same spot and the runway began to break up!

567.   Answer: 2 out of 3. You know you don't have the second bag, but because the first bag has two white eggs, you could have picked either; you can think of it as four eggs in total in two bags (1 and 3), three white and one brown; there are 3 eggs left 2 of which are white.

568.   3 hours and 3 minutes.

569.   Black. Explanation: the man at the back can see both the hats worn by the two men in front of him, so if both of those hats were white, he would know that the hat he wore must be black (there are only 2 white hats). Since he does not answer, he must see at least one black hat ahead of him. Once the man in the middle realizes that the man at the back cannot work out what he is wearing, he knows that there must be at least one black hat worn by himself and the man at the front of the line of 3. So, if the middle man saw a white hat in front of him, he would know that his own hat was black and could answer the question correctly, but since he does not answer, he must see a black hat on the man in front. When it becomes apparent to the man in front that neither of the men behind him can answer the question, he realizes that the middle man saw a black hat in front of him and is able to say that his hat is black.

570.   Richard Douglas Fosbury revolutionized the sport of high jumping by replacing the straddle (face down) traditional approach with an innovative backward (face up) style that became known as the "Fosbury flop."

571.   Make a triangle with 3 matches. Add 1 match in the middle to split the equilateral triangle into two isosceles triangles. Then make a mirror image of that below (with 3 matches) to create a diamond shape.

572.   Take away the two sticks in the lower left corner and the one stick at the top of the middle square in the top row; you end up with 3 squares in a V shape with just 2 corners touching.

573. The trick that few people guess when they first try this test is that you do not need to stay within the boundaries of the dots; you can start and finish outside ("out of the box"). Start in the bottom right corner, place your pencil tip on that dot and trace a line diagonally to the top left corner, cutting through 2 more dots as you do that, then turn south / downwards and draw a line towards the bottom left corner, through the 2 dots on the left side of the 9-dot square but do not stop, imagine there is another dot below the three in the first column, continue the straight line to it. Now aim for another imaginary dot to the right of the right corner and draw a straight line diagonally towards it. Then turn left and draw a horizontal line to the top left dot. You have done it!

574. Take away the two outside circles / balls from the first level and move them to join the 2 on level 3. Move the top (apex) circle / ball to the level below level 1.

575. Two half-full barrels are poured into one of the empty barrels. Another two half-full barrels are poured into another of the empty barrels. This produces nine full barrels, three half-full barrels, and nine empty barrels. Each son will get: three full barrels, one half-full barrel, and three empty barrels.

576. The Water Level Goes Down! 1 liter of water has a mass of 1 kg. When the brick is in the boat, it is forcing the water to be displaced by 2 kg or as we know 2 ltr. When the brick is sitting on the bottom of the lake, it is displacing just its own volume or one liter.

577. In ancient times, wise women practiced the healing arts throughout Europe, mostly as midwives, until they became

the target of the church and the state. The Macbeth witches brewed ingredients that are plants: Eye of Newt is a common name for mustard seed (Brassica nigra), Toe of frog = Buttercup (Ranunculus acris L.), Wool of bat = Holly Leaves (Ilex aquifolium) or moss, Tongue of dog = Gypsyflower Hound's Tooth (Cynoglossum officinale L.), Adders fork = Violet or Least Adder's-tongue (Ophioglossum lusitanicum L.), Blind-worm = Knotweed or Slowworm (Anguis fragilis), Lizard's leg – Ivy (Hedera), Howlet's wing – garlic (Allium sativum) or maybe ginger.

578. The 3 candidates were told that each of them would be given either a red or a blue mark. They had to raise their hands if they saw a red mark on another candidate and all three candidates raised their hands. After the candidates had looked at each other for a few minutes without working out the solution, one candidate announced the correct answer and won. So how did they do it? Firstly, if two people had blue marks, one person's hand would not be raised. Secondly, if candidate 1 had seen a blue mark on candidate 2 and a red mark on candidate 3, then candidate 1 would have known immediately that their own mark must be red. Thus, any candidate who sees a blue mark can guess at once. Finally, the winner realizes that since no one guesses at once, there must be no blue marks, so every mark must be red.

579. The young woman is Dorothy from the film "The Wizard of Oz".

580. Answer = "Are Your Lights On?"

581. Maybe both necessity and laziness are the mothers of invention (excluding Frank Zappa's group). Vermont

resident Paul Wallich developed a drone to monitor his son's 400-yard walk to the bus during the cold winter months. He built the drone with a smartphone video feed, put a GPS in his son's backpack and wrote about the project in a technology journal.

582. You should switch. This puzzle is similar to a probability puzzle known as the Monty Hall problem, the original host of the TV show "Let's Make a Deal". Many people, including some mathematicians, do not believe the solution until they see the results of tests. If you switch, you have about a 2 in 3 chance of winning the car, whereas if you stick to your original choice, you have about a 1 in 3 chance. This has been proved again and again with math's simulations. The odds are better if you switch because Monty manages the remaining choices; he knows where the car is. He never chooses the door with the car. And by organizing the remaining doors for you, he raises the odds that switching is always a good bet.

583. Corey Taylor, a private consultant from Chicago, faked his own death to try to avoid paying $175 to break his contract with Verizon, his phone service provider. He typed a fake death certificate and had a friend send it off to the provider. Unfortunately for him, Verizon's billing department saw through this scheme.

584. Instead of stacking the boxes on top of each other, the chimp went to the scientist, took his hand and gently invited him to stand below the bunch of bananas, then climbed on his shoulders and reached the bananas!

585. Thinking quickly, the prince reaches into the velvet bag and, as he draws one of the pebbles out, he fumbles and

drops it. That pebble becomes indistinguishable as it joins all the others on the ground. The Prince apologizes for being so clumsy and points out politely that the pebble that is still in the bag (the one he did not choose) must be the other color (i.e., black). It is an elegant solution because the King is unable to contradict him yet saves face and the Prince wins the Princess (and as a bonus, is not executed!) Will they live happily ever after?

586.   The Egg, dinosaurs laid eggs long before there were any chickens.

587.   The lawyer asked the translator to sign different questions to those being asked verbally to see if the man answers the spoken words or the sign language. He proved the van driver was pretending to be deaf.

588.   Switch #1 on and leave it on for 5 minutes, then switch it off, turn #2 switch on and walk into the room. If the light is on, it is #2; if it is off, feel the light bulb – if it is warm or hot, it was switch # 1; if the bulb is not on and cold, it must be switch #3.

589.   Thinking that America was becoming a den of iniquity, he invented the Switchback Gravity Railway roller coaster as a distraction from temptations. Disgusted with the increasing number of what he saw were hedonistic amusements, LaMarcus Adna Thompson looked for something that would draw people away from the taverns, gambling parlors, dance halls, and brothels that were becoming increasingly popular as the nation grew prosperous after the Civil War. Within three weeks of opening, he was making about six hundred dollars a day. These were slow, gravity-powered cars that faced outward, rather than forward, so one could enjoy the view as the car coasted at less than 6 MPH, not as scary or thrilling as the ones available today!

590. This is a very difficult puzzle. It has been discussed many times since Danish computer scientist Peter Bro Milter Sen first proposed the problem in 2003. If every prisoner selects 50 drawers at random, the probability that a single prisoner finds their number is 50%, which means that the probability that all prisoners will find their numbers is ($\frac{1}{2}$)100 or about 0.000,000,000,000,000,000,000,000,000,8. So, is the situation hopeless? Well, no, there is a strategy that offers a survival probability of more than 30%. If each prisoner begins by opening the drawer labeled with their own number, then look at the number in the first drawer and open the drawer with that number next and so on, repeat until the prisoner finds his own number or, after 50 attempts, fails. By starting with their own number, the prisoner guarantees they are on the unique permutation cycle of drawers. The only question is whether this cycle is longer than fifty drawers. What would happen if they were each allowed to withdraw their own number from a drawer – if they found it?

591. You could try to do the right thing - look after the old lady and make a good impression on your soul mate - by acting compassionately (and possibly saving the old lady who might die). The clever approach might be to give the car keys to your good friend and let him take the old woman home or to the hospital. You stay behind and wait for the bus with the partner of your dreams (share the coffee and give them the blanket).

592. The new software (an addition to the existing guidance program), was aimed at dealing with the possibility of a torpedo going out of control. It should self-destruct if, for some reason, it headed back towards the ship that fired it.

The new program code instructed the torpedo to blow itself up if the system turned 180 degrees from the direction it was fired. The idea seemed fine in theory. Trouble was that when a torpedo got stuck in the firing tube on board the ship, the captain ordered the ship to turn back to port – BANG.

593. Fill the beaker with water before you go to the city and pour it out when you get there; local air will take its place, naturally. (You could also take some balloons and a bicycle pump).

594. The Prisoner's Dilemma poses questions about friendship, loyalty and rational behaviour. In this scenario, loyalty to a partner is irrational, even though mutual cooperation would yield a greater net reward. The best strategy for two rational prisoners is betrayal. Regardless of what the other decides, each prisoner gets a higher reward by betraying the other. If one of them betrays the other, they will get a sentence of either zero or 5 years, whereas if that person stays silent, they will get either 10 years or 2 years. This is also evident in the "Tragedy of the Commons". Aristotle wrote that "That which is common to the greatest number gets the least amount of care. Men pay most attention to what is their own: they care less for what is common." In fact, cooperative behavior does occur far more often than this game suggests. People tend to trust each other and work together to search for and achieve the best common outcome.

595. Who drinks water? Who owns the zebra? Answer = Assuming that one person drinks water and one owns a zebra, then it is possible not only to deduce the answers to the two questions but to figure out a complete solution of

who lives where, in what color house, keeping what pet, drinking what drink, and smoking what brand of cigarettes. By considering the clues a few at a time, it is possible to slowly build inferences that incrementally complete the puzzle's unique correct solution. For example, by clue 10, the Norwegian lives in house #1, and by clue 15, house #2 must be blue. The Norwegian's house therefore cannot be blue, nor can it be red, where the Englishman lives (clue 2), or green or ivory, which are next to each other (clue 6). It must therefore be yellow, which means the Norwegian also smokes Kools (clue 8).

House	1	2	3	4	5
Color	Yellow	Blue	Red	Irony	Green
Nationality	Norwegian	Ukrainian	Englishmen	Spaniard	Japanese
Drink	Water	Tea	Milk	Orange Juice	Coffee
Smoke	Kools	Chesterfield	Old Gold	Lucky Strike	Parliament
Pet	Fox	Horse	Snails	Dog	Zebra

596. The barometer question.

- Answer 1: Tie the barometer to a long roll of string, take it to the top of the building and lower the barometer down to the ground. Make a mark on the string and measure the length of the string and barometer. The height of the building is equal to the length of the string and the barometer.

- Answer 2: Drop the barometer from the top of the building and time its fall with a stopwatch.

- Answer 3: On a sunny day, measure the height of the barometer relative to the length of its shadow, then measure the length of the building's shadow and use the same ratio to work out the height of the building.

- Answer 4: Use the barometer itself as a unit of measure. Measure its height and then, laboriously and progressively, count how many barometers high the building is by climbing the stairs and marking off barometer lengths as you go.

- Answer 5: Find the building's architectural plans or ask the building superintendent. You could offer to give the barometer as a gift to obtain this information.

- Answer 6: Use the barometer to measure the air pressure at the bottom and at the top of the building, then use the formula $p = p_0 e^{-ay}$ that takes into account the amount that pressure reduces as height increases.

597. Some ideas and solutions that come to mind include:

- Send a lift engineer to check the motors and pulley mechanisms.

- Sue the architect.

- Speed the lifts up and allow less time on each floor.

- Upgrade the software so that the lifts work more efficiently and learn to anticipate demands.

- Stop so many people entering the building.

- Suggest that staff do not all work a 9 to 5 day so that lift usage will be more spread out. Staff will be pleased to be given flexible working hours and will not all arrive, go for lunch and leave at the same times.

- Find out why they move up and down so much and provide what they need closer to where they are.

- Do a thorough study of lift usage so that a new strategy can be developed to reorganize the occupancy of the building.

- Cut 2 new lift shafts vertically though the building and double the number of lifts.

- Add more lifts by attaching them on the outside of the building.

- Make one of the lifts an express – meant to carry people up or down 5 floors at a time.

- Make the lifts multi story, i.e., add another lift compartment above or below the existing ones.

- Convince the people who occupy the building that the apparently slow lifts provide a great excuse to get more exercise and that exercise is good for them. Having slow lifts is actually a benefit. Put up notices that explain the value of exercise and how many calories are burned when climbing a flight of stairs.

- Create competitive league tables with time challenges for running up and down stairs. People will want to avoid the lifts in order to train and get faster.

- Another tactic might be to persuade the occupants to relax more – that slower lifts offer the chance to slow the day down a bit, take time out, reflect and meditate.

- Adopt a different approach by providing mirrors and whiteboards on every floor, beside the lift entrances, so that people do not get bored and frustrated so quickly. Time will seem to pass less noticeably slowly as they look at themselves, check their clothes, hair and make-up and add notes, cartoons and drawings to the boards.

- Put coffee stations next to the lifts on alternate floors so that occupants start to think of the lift areas as convivial, social places and enjoy spending time there.

- Build a sky bridge across to a neighboring building and use their lifts.

- Sell the building to someone else, give them the problem.

- Knock the building down and start again.

598. The purposes of a cat: a cuddly, furry friend; an alarm clock / device for waking you up, to be a favorite topic of conversation, to act as an endless source of photographs and videos; to sustain a position as a social media content provider; to dress up in silly costumes for our amusement, a thing to clog vacuum cleaners; a vicious killing machine; a vermin controller; an entertainment provider; a stress reduction system and a tool for lowering blood-pressure; something to buy cat food and presents for; as a way to fund vets and pet related businesses, to provide an animal to do experiments and vivisection on; a way to get firefighters and others to climb trees, a manufacturer of

kittens – a potential source of income; to occupy a god-like status to be revered and honored (as in ancient Egypt)……

599. Dogs and horses have long and honorable associations with mankind as: loyal and lifelong companions; they offer love, emotional support and act as good listeners; make us exercise more; usually make us happier and more attractive; help to stave off loneliness and social isolation, provide us with excuses and opportunities to make friends; help us cope in a crisis and live longer; can be beasts of burden, are used as transport pullers of sleds and carriages; as police assistants; as herders (sheepdogs / cowboy quarter-horses); in wars; for races (greyhounds / racehorses); and for gambling / betting; as willing servants and pupils for training; working as guards and gun dog retrievers / in ploughing teams; in showing and other classes (Crufts / county fairs and horse of the year), for exploration and rescues; in circuses; in competitions (flyball and sheepdog trials / dressage, show jumping, cross country, working equitation); as slaves that have little choice in what they are allowed to do and depend on their owners for food, shelter and care.

600. Did you make a decision about what you would do if faced with the ethical dilemma of whether to pull the lever and redirect the train? This example is often used in lectures and discussions about ethics and more recently, in scenarios that envisage potential problem situations that autonomous / self-drive cars might encounter, such as what to do if a child crosses the road and there is not space to stop – the brakes will not halt the car before it hits the child – so is it best to turn onto the sidewalk / pavement

and what if that would put the life of the person in the car (the owner) or pedestrians at risk?

TREASURE HUNT

Outline: This is a virtual Geocaching / scavenger hunt challenge. Many of the clues you solve lead to the next until the final location is revealed.

Geocaching is a worldwide treasure-hunting pastime, possibly based on a game called letterboxing which began as long ago as 1854. Participants decipher hints and coded messages to find objects hidden in specific locations and landmarks. In a scavenger hunt, contestants are given clues or riddles that lead them to specific locations where they can find the next clue. The game involves driving or moving from one clue to another until the final objective or treasure is found.

This Treasure Hunt Challenge is a virtual hunt you can take part in where ever you are in the world (assuming you can access the internet). To win the prize, you must work your way through a sequence of coded clues and, as it were, move from one place to another, getting closer to the final destination. You need to identify the final location and rearrange the first letters of all the locations you have "visited" to make 2 words. You might like to track your adventure with Google Earth. All the places and locations in this challenge have been mentioned somewhere in the book.

Instructions: These clues use different ciphers. The first 4 are pretty straightforward. You should be able to figure out which place or location each cipher code is referring to. You need the answer to the 4th clue to progress to the 5th. Use that 9-letter place name to work out the next location in the sequence. When you have found the fifth location use that name to determine the next clue, and so on. Clues 5 to 10 all follow a similar format. You will need to use "What 3 Words" to solve the final clue. (Clues 1, 2, 3 and 4 are quite different to clues 5 to 10).

Clue 1: Y V F O B A

Clue 2: 13 5 12 2 15 21 18 14 5

Clue 3: G R U O B M E X U L

Clue 4: V W R M Y F I T S

Clue 5: D O H I C F B G E J M Q L K

Clue 6: Q A N E B F D J K

Clue 7: Q R T H G A M I S Y

Clue 8: J F N D I H Q M R

Clue 9: D O K N S J W I

Clue 10: K J T H, Q K M C Y Q, C V C M E

Facebook page = 600 Puzzles

info@middlepartacademy.com

Printed in Great Britain
by Amazon

35148834R00139